Kids SPEAK 10

chaim walder

Translated by
Aviva Rappaport

Illustrated by
Devorah Benedict

FELDHEIM PUBLISHERS

Originally published in 2018 in Hebrew as
Yeladim Mesaprim al Atzmam (Vol. 10)

First published 2018
ISBN 978-1-68025-335-1

Translated by Aviva Rappaport
Illustrated by Devorah Benedict

Feldheim Publishers
POB 43163 / Jerusalem, Israel

208 Airport Executive Park
Nanuet, NY 10954

www.feldheim.com

DISTRIBUTED IN EUROPE BY:
Lehmanns
+44-0-191-430-0333
info@lehmanns.co.uk
www.lehmanns.co.uk

DISTRIBUTED IN AUSTRALIA BY:
Golds World of Judaica
+613 95278775
info@golds.com.au
www.golds.com.au

Printed in Israel

To my beloved son Rabbi David נ"י,
my daughter-in-law Sarah תחי',
and their daughter, Esther Leah תחי'—
who are the sweet smile of the family!

———————

Contents

Preface.. 9

My Electric Bike...................................... 13

Responsibility 23

Wearing the Mask 34

The Train of Fear 53

Bike Mystery 71

Groups at War...................................... 82

A Bas Mitzvah to Remember 98

The Gift of Patience............................ 120

The Real Winner.................................. 134

Was That an Invitation?....................... 149

The Contact Lens................................. 165

The Saddest Birthday Boy.................... 178

The Answers in the Coat Pocket 194

Being the Real Me 209

Glossary 223

Preface

When I was younger, I taught fourth-grade boys. In that framework, I encountered a boy who hit other children. I tried to influence him through various means, from pleasant persuasion to punishment, with no success. Then I asked him to write down what he was feeling.

The boy wrote five lines, and with his permission, I developed those five lines into a story that gave expression to what he was feeling. I hoped that by this means the boy would get the message and calm down.

The boy was very excited by the story because he felt that someone understood him. At his request, I read the story to the class. The students were glued to their seats, and the message was absorbed. The boys realized that their friend didn't hate them and didn't want to hit them. He was just looking for a way to connect. They gave him the opportunity to become part of the group, and his behavior improved.

Thanks to the short story he wrote, a story that talked about his feelings, the boy had the opportunity of a lifetime.

And he wasn't the only one. I, too, got the opportunity a lifetime.

That story and the impact it had on my student made me realize the great benefit of children saying what's in their hearts and expressing their feelings. I told my students that there's no point in keeping everything inside, in burying one's feelings. I told them that if they did have any feelings buried inside, they were invited to write them to me, and I would turn their few lines into a story. The kids were excited, and I started to write stories about the emotions my students expressed. I would read them the stories and so helped them understand what their friends were going through.

At the end of the year, several parents asked me to print the stories as a book. I hesitated at first. I was afraid no one would be interested in it. Finally, I overcame my fear and published the first *Kids Speak* book.

It turns out that my fears were misplaced. Children enjoyed *Kids Speak* tremendously, and letters began pouring in to POB 211 in Bnei Brak. From these letters came more and more stories that gave voice to the children's feelings.

Since then, twenty-five years have passed. Following that first book, I've published another forty-seven books—for toddlers, children, youth, and adults—but the Kids Speak series remains the flagship that captured children's hearts. The books have been translated into eight languages, and today, with *siyata d'Shemaya*, Kids All Over the World Speak.

I am very moved to publish the book you hold in your hands, the tenth book in the series.

Everyone now realizes that Kids Speak is not just a series of books but a way of life. *To tell. To talk. To express.* Not to keep things locked up inside.

I thank the Creator of the World for allowing me to help children (and adults) convey what weighs on their hearts, express their feelings, and share with others what's going on inside. I believe that this helps them to be calmer, happier, stronger, and better.

Chaim Walder
Chanukah 5778

My Electric Bike

My name is Eliad.

I'm thirteen, and I live in Beersheva.

Two years ago, I asked my parents to buy me an electric bicycle for an *afikoman* present.

They said no. They said it was too dangerous for someone my age.

I told them some kids in my school already had one. My parents found that hard to believe, so I gave them some names. I was sure they'd agree once they realized I would be the only one without one.

I was wrong.

They listened to my long list but still said, "We don't approve of giving you an electric bike at your age."

I was very upset. "So why did I give you all those

names? Why do I have to be the only one without one?" I started crying. "Why do all my friends' parents let, but not mine?" I said lots of things I now regret in an effort to pressure my parents into buying me the bike I wanted.

My parents knew that when I was determined to get something, I'd drive them crazy until I got it, so my father said to me, "We're not going to argue with you. This is what we decided. End of discussion."

*   *   *

So there I was, without an electric bicycle.

More and more of my friends were getting electric bikes. I kept on begging my parents to buy me one, until finally, I guess they couldn't take it anymore. I knew that my parents had my safety in mind, but that didn't make a difference to me. Besides, by last Pesach over half the class had electric bikes. My father said that since I had waited so long for this and still wanted it so badly after all this time, he'd buy me one.

The bike was bought, and I was flying high.

Kids don't tell their parents everything. It took me a while, but eventually, I realized that my parents were totally right about the bike. I came to that conclusion after finding myself bumping into parked cars and worse, little kids. Every week there was another incident. My friends had the same things happen to them. We felt guilty about it and knew it was wrong to continue using the electric bikes this way, but we didn't tell our parents, though we should have, because we knew what would happen if we did.

One afternoon about two months ago, I heard knocking on the front door.

My mother went to see who it was. Suddenly I heard her say, "My Eliad? Impossible."

I heard a man's voice say, "Several witnesses say it was him. We want you to come down to the police station."

My mother called me. At the front door stood a police officer. My jaw dropped.

"Are you Eliad?" he asked. "Yes."

"Did you ride your bike last week?"

"Yes," I said. "I ride my bike almost every day."

"Okay, but a week ago you hit an elderly man and then you fled the scene."

"That's not true," I said.

"We have witnesses who say it was you."

"But it wasn't me," I said.

"So who was it?"

"I have no idea," I said. "All I know is that I didn't

knock anyone down, certainly not an elderly man."

"No problem," the policeman said. "Please come with me, along with your mother. Before we go, I want to see your bicycle."

I started to cry. The three of us went outside, and the policeman photographed the bike from all angles.

At the police station, they questioned me like a common criminal: when did I ride, how did I ride, if I knew that riding an electric bike under the age of sixteen is illegal. But that wasn't all. They started asking me questions about the elderly man who fell. I insisted that I didn't know what they were talking about.

After a while, the policemen left the room leaving me alone with my mother.

"Eliad, tell me the truth," my mother said. "We'll deal with it, but we have to know the truth. They won't lock you up because they don't do that to kids your age."

"Wait a minute, Ima," I said. "Don't you believe me?"

When my mother didn't reply, I realized that she wasn't sure I was telling the truth.

"Ima," I said, "even if they put me in jail for a hundred years, I didn't knock down any elderly man! I hope he recovers quickly, and I feel terrible that he was injured—but I didn't hurt him! If you don't believe me, there's nothing else I can do."

My mother looked at me. I could tell that now she believed me.

The policeman returned.

"My son denies it," my mother told him. "If you have any evidence, tell us what it is. In the meantime, I think we're free to leave."

"You two can go home," the policeman said, "but before you do, I'm going to give your husband a ticket with a fine of one thousand shekels plus eight points on his driver's license."

"What! Why?" my mother asked.

"That's the law. The father of a minor who rides an electric bicycle gets a ticket—and just you wait. This is only the beginning. You can look forward to being sued by the elderly man who was bruised and hurt. You're free to go now."

On the way home, my mother called my father.

My father couldn't believe it. "If my son broke the law, why are they putting it on my license?"

"Your son didn't break the law," my mother corrected him.

By the time my father came home that evening, he had more information. The law here is that the father of a youth under the age of sixteen who rides an electric bicycle gets a ticket, and if the rider injures someone, his parents must defend themselves against the lawsuit, because an e-bike is not insured.

My father spoke to a lawyer, who told him that because the policeman didn't see me riding the bike, he couldn't issue a ticket. As for the elderly man who was knocked down, the lawyer said that since the policeman didn't give any details, apparently they didn't have solid evidence.

But within a month we received a registered letter telling us we were being sued for over half a million shekels for injuries suffered by the elderly man.

I can't describe what I—and my parents—felt. From out of nowhere, we were facing a huge lawsuit for something I hadn't done.

My parents hired a lawyer. He contacted the police and asked how they came to the conclusion that I was to blame.

They said they had witnesses.

The lawyer demanded to be allowed to question the witnesses. When he did, most of them said they weren't sure it was me. That invalidated their testimony. One of them, though, insisted that he was sure it was me because he recognized my blue bicycle with the black bike bag.

"Did you see Eliad riding the bike?" the lawyer asked him.

"I only saw him from the back, but I recognized his bike," the man said.

The lawyer said we needed stronger proof that it wasn't me. He went to stores near the incident and asked if they had CCTV monitors, and then asked those that did if he could watch their video covering the time the elderly man was injured.

Three hours later, he discovered the truth.

It was my bike, but the person riding it was a kid who had taken it without permission.

The video was shown to the judge, who immediately dismissed all charges against me and my parents, including the ticket.

The charges were now brought against the other kid, who had to explain why he took a bicycle that didn't belong to him and why he knocked down an elderly man and then ran away without getting him help. Running away was a much more serious charge, because knocking down the man was an accident—a terrible one!—but abandoning him was deliberate.

Now he and his parents were in big trouble, but I had learned my lesson. We sold the bike. It wasn't appropriate for a kid my age.

Because this happened to me, I feel a responsibility to share it with everyone. Did you know that last year, here in Eretz Yisrael where I live, 275 people were injured from riding an electric bike?

Kids under the age of sixteen aren't allowed to ride an electric bike. These bikes are dangerous (and I think you know it without me even telling you), and they can injure other people as well.

Even regular bikes can be dangerous, but at least they're legal. And if we listen to our parents' advice regarding our safety, wear a bike helmet, and follow the laws and regulations for responsible bike riding, our chances of harming ourselves or pedestrians will be much lower.

Responsibility

My name is Yael.

I'm thirteen, and I live in Givat Shmuel.

I'm popular and adventurous, and I'd rather play with my friends than do anything else.

I've got only one problem: I'm not very responsible.

When my parents ask me to do something, I don't always follow through. Or, to be more correct, I usually don't follow through.

I'm not talking about things like cleaning up my room. My parents practically gave up on that. I'm talking about tasks that require responsibility, like watching my little three-year-old brother, Shimmy.

It would usually start with me arguing with my mother that I didn't want to watch him. If my mother insisted, I'd take him outside with me and watch him for a few minutes. Then I'd tell him, "Go play over there. I have to go somewhere for a minute."

Lots of times that "minute" would turn out to be a good twenty minutes, and when I'd come back I'd discover that in the meantime Shimmy had gone back home by himself. That was the best-case scenario. The worst was when he would cry, drawing the attention of half the neighborhood. Everyone would look at me critically, wordlessly accusing me, as if to say, "What kind of an irresponsible girl are you?"

And then came the time I want to tell you about.

This time, Shimmy didn't go back home or stand there and cry. He decided to go look for me.

When my mother came down after a while and asked me where Shimmy was, I didn't even remember where I'd left him. We started looking feverishly for him. When we didn't find him, we asked half the neighborhood to help us. I felt awful. I knew that no one would forgive me for what I'd done. But if, *chas v'shalom*, something happened to Shimmy, I'd never forgive myself.

Shimmy had disappeared. Several hours later, we found him.

He'd crossed dangerous streets, gone in and out of buildings, and finally—you won't believe it—climbed

up two flights of stairs in an apartment building and knocked on the door.

Baruch Hashem, the door he knocked on was opened by a woman who could have been his grand-mother. The woman somehow got my mother's phone number, and we raced over there. Shimmy looked fine, considering the hours he'd been lost.

My mother hugged him and asked him why he hadn't waited for me, his big sister Yaeli.

What did he say? That he'd gone looking for me because he thought I'd gotten lost.

I knew that this time no one would forgive me for being so irresponsible.

My mother thanked the woman and turned to leave, but the woman stopped her. "It seems that there's a bit of a problem here with someone's lack of responsibility."

My cheeks burned and tears sprang to my eyes.

"Perhaps your daughter can remain here for ten minutes or so," the woman said. "I want to tell her a story. I'm almost certain that once she hears it, she'll change, *b'ezras Hashem*."

"Why not?" my mother said. "Should I stay too?"

"Actually," the woman said. "I want to speak to her privately. I'd prefer if you wait right outside the kitchen for a few minutes."

That's how I wound up staying there with the woman who had found Shimmy. Or, to be more exact, the woman that Shimmy had found. We sat at the kitchen table, and she started to tell me the story…

* * *

"As you can see," she told me, "I am no longer young, and I can hardly see. In fact, I'm almost blind. I can see shadows but nothing more. I can't travel alone, and I can only walk through the neighborhood very slowly.

"For many years, I'd dreamed of traveling to Europe to visit *kivrei tzaddikim* and enjoy a vacation. When a friend visited me, I asked her if she wanted to join me.

"My friend said that her state of health didn't allow her to make the trip. Right then, an idea flashed through her mind and she said, 'I have a granddaughter who's nineteen who'd love to go to Europe, but her parents can't afford it. How about if she joins you and helps you with your trip?'

"'That's an excellent idea,' I said. 'I'll pay for her ticket and all expenses, and in exchange, she'll accompany me and help me.'

"Right then and there my friend called her granddaughter. The girl was delighted and said it was a real opportunity for her to fulfill her dream of traveling to Europe. She said that she'd stay by my side every step of the way. All she asked was that I accompany her to several places she'd always dreamed of seeing. I agreed and said I'd pay her ticket and expenses.

"We set a date and bought tickets. Before the trip, I bought the girl expensive new luggage, and I sent her to buy some new clothes so it wouldn't remain empty. In other words, I spoiled her."

"I only wish it could have been me," I said. It was a great story.

"We landed at ten o'clock in the morning," the elderly woman continued, "and took a taxi to our hotel. Until this point, everything was fine.

"At the hotel, the girl said to me, 'Listen, one of my friends is here in town. She also came for a vacation. I'll just hop over to say hello and be right back.'

"I agreed," the elderly woman said. "I even felt glad that she had a friend. It's just that her 'hopping over' could have won a prize because it lasted for nine hours.

"Do you understand? She left at eleven in the morning and came back at eight at night! I was sick with anxiety. I didn't know what had happened to her. Was she kidnapped? In a terrorist attack? I was so frightened that I forgot I was hungry and didn't eat a thing.

"Suddenly, she appeared, very apologetic. 'I'm so sorry,' she said. 'My friend dragged me with her to see a few sites. I didn't notice how much time passed.'

"It took me a long time to calm down," the elderly woman told me. "The girl promised sincerely that such a thing would never happen again and that the next day she would stay with me the entire time. Well, she promised, but she didn't promise to keep her promise."

"The following day, she took me to the *kever* of a tzaddik, but she kept urging me to finish davening as quickly as possible. Then she brought me back to the hotel and disappeared again until the evening."

"I don't believe it!" I said, starting to feel angry at a girl I didn't even know.

"A whole week went by like that, with her spending a total of maybe four hours with me.

"When I saw that instead of going to *kivrei tzaddikim* I was trapped in my hotel room, I called the airline to move up my flight a day earlier. They agreed—for a hefty fee. We flew home together a day earlier than planned. I spent the flight fuming and didn't exchange even one word with that girl who had taken advantage of me, left me alone, and deeply hurt my feelings. At

the airport, I didn't even want to share a taxi with her. I gave her some money and told her, 'I'll manage on my own. I don't want to see you or hear from you ever again.'

"That's the story," the elderly woman said. "You can do with it what you want."

I started crying. I knew why she'd told me the story.

She leaned over and patted my shoulder. "I don't think you're like her. There's a big difference between the two of you. You're only thirteen, and she's already nineteen. It's not the same at all. But I do think that if someone had stopped her when she was thirteen, maybe she wouldn't have become so selfish and irresponsible. Don't you agree?"

I nodded.

*   *   *

"What do I do now?" I heard myself ask.

"I have an idea," the elderly woman said. "But before I tell you what it is, I want to ask you something. Do you think I should forgive that girl for treating me that way?"

I thought about it and then said, "No. I think there's no forgiving or excusing such behavior."

"That's what I thought too," the elderly woman

said. "But before Rosh Hashanah, I went to ask a *rav*.
I told him everything that happened. He was shocked
and said it was hard for him to answer, but after a few
minutes he smiled and said to me, 'You know what?
The terrible story you just told me has a deep message.'

"I didn't know what he meant, so he explained.

"'What you went through is a *mashal* of our connection with Hashem. Every day we say Modeh Ani. At the
end we say '*rabbah Emunasecha*—great is Your faithfulness'—meaning Hashem's faithfulness. Why don't we
say *rabba emunaseinu*—great is our faithfulness?

"'As you know,' the *rav* continued, 'every night a
trial is held. Everyone's *neshamah* promises to fix the
person's deeds and to cling to Hashem and His mitzvos. And Hashem returns our *neshamos* to us, and we
wake up in the morning to a new day.

"'Do we keep our promises? Not always! And then
comes the next night, when we promise again. And
again, we don't keep our promises. Now, pay attention.
Look how angry you were after five days when someone
didn't keep her word. Think about how angry Hashem
could be with all His creations, especially the older ones,
who have made Him promises every night, yet don't
fulfill them in the morning. Days, weeks, months, a year
goes by and He still trusts us and forgives us.

"'That's why we thank Him as soon as we open our eyes. We say, "Thank You so much, Hashem, for giving me back my *neshamah* because You took pity on me and You believed in me, even though I don't deserve it because I broke my promises to You so many times."

"'Hashem forgives us,' the *rav* added, 'even though we break our promises so many times and distance ourselves from Him again. So maybe you, too, can find the strength to forgive that girl who didn't act responsibly, and believe that she has changed.'"

* * *

The elderly woman looked at me, and I knew, without her saying another word, that the story she told me and the lesson that could be learned from it would change me forever. From that day on, I took it upon myself to be more responsible and to act more mature.

I decided to tell other kids this amazing story that happened to me. I'm sure that tomorrow morning when you say Modeh Ani, you'll understand its special meaning much more fully.

Wearing the Mask

My name is Gadi.

I'm thirteen years old, and in eighth grade. I live in Hadera.

I haven't told anyone this story, though it happened a year ago. Only one other boy knows about it, and you'll soon see why. It's because he's also connected to the story.

I suggest you drop everything to read this carefully because you've never heard a story like this before in your life.

* * *

I'm considered a very popular boy. I'm not saying that to brag, but because it's very important to the story.

The truth is, I never thought about it too much. Being popular was just part of who I was.

I'm the kid everyone waits for before they start the game, the one who decides what we're playing, where we're going and when, and who's invited to come along.

Surrounding me were all the class VIPs. As for the rest, we just ignored them. I never even gave them a passing thought. I just lived my life with the friends I chose to be with. Let the others hang around with whoever they wanted.

I supposed there might have been kids over the years whose feelings I hurt, mostly the ones I suspected of trying to break into our group. Like, for instance, the boys who tried to eavesdrop on our conversations or join a fun activity we'd decided to have.

As far as I was concerned, I didn't even feel like I was hurting anyone's feelings because my whole life I'd been used to doing what I wanted and having everyone follow my lead—meaning, only the boys I *wanted* to follow my lead.

I could go on and on describing how things were, but I think you've got the idea.

* * *

Last year, my family vacationed in the Galilee. We hiked along a marked trail, and then we went to an Arab village that had a huge mall made especially for families with kids. Inside it was an amusement park, so that while the parents shopped the kids could play.

Suddenly I saw Shauli, a boy in my class.

Shauli is a quiet, shy kid, and I don't think I've exchanged a single word with him since first grade.

Sometimes kids called him "Shauli Galoshes." Why? Who knows! When they called him that, he'd act hurt and withdrawn, but that didn't exactly make the others stop.

I don't think I ever called him "Shauli Galoshes," but not because I was a nice, considerate boy. It was because I was so far away from him that I didn't even deem it worth my while to give him any attention at all.

I know that what I'm writing here sounds arrogant, but I'm just telling the truth.

Included in this attitude of superiority was not even saying hello.

"Hey, Gadi," my brother called to me at the mall's amusement park, "isn't that a boy from your class?"

"Shhh," I said to him. "What business is it of yours?" (As you can see, I wasn't all that polite to my brother, either.)

We went from ride to ride. Every few minutes I passed by Shauli as if he didn't exist.

* * *

At one point, I saw a bunch of kids gathered around a man.

I went closer and saw something I'd never seen before.

There was a sign saying "Mask Artist." It took me a minute to figure out what the man knew how to do, but from then on, I was glued to the spot.

His craft was very interesting. He would put a type of clay or wax on a child's face and then smooth it over the face until it became a mask that exactly matched the child's features. After removing it from the child's face, he would put something that looked like a nylon balloon over the mask. It hardened onto the mask instantly, and he would paint the child's portrait on it. At the end of the process, the child got an exact copy of his face.

It was fascinating and totally amazing. What a great idea for Purim! But the more I thought about it, the more I realized that it wasn't such a good idea. *What would be so great about it?* I thought. *Why would a kid need a mask that looked just like him? His own face is a better copy, so what would be the point?*

No sooner had I asked myself that question than the answer leaped out at me.

I had the most fantastic idea! And I knew I just had to do it.

I began imagining the costume, and the further I went with the fantasy, the more excited I got about my idea.

In case you didn't catch on, let me explain.

True, there's no point in a kid pretending to be himself, but what if two kids made masks and switched between them? That would be the most perfect disguise you could dream of.

No sooner had I thought of it than I hit a snag. The idea needed two boys in the same class with masks made by this same craftsman. That meant the boy needed to be here, right now.

Wait a second! Shauli was here!

I winced. Shauli? What did I have to do with him? After a little more thought, a huge grin split my face.

That wasn't a problem. That made it perfect! Shauli was the last person my classmates would think I had any kind of connection with, let alone something as important and secretive as a Purim costume. For one day, I'd be Shauli, and Shauli would be Gadi. And if we did it well, it would be the best costume not only of that year but of the next decade.

I'm sure you can see what a great idea it was.

Without batting an eyelash, I went over to Shauli and said to him, "Hey there, Shauli. What's doing?"

Shauli blushed in confusion and then turned pale. I'd never spoken to him before about anything.

"Okaaaay," he said.

"Having fun?" I asked.

"Yes. I mean, sure. It's fun."

"Shauli, I have an idea. What do you think about both of us getting masks done here and then in another month, on Purim, you'll wear my mask, and I'll wear yours?"

Poor Shauli. I could see by his expression that the idea frightened him.

"Uh...okay... Sure... Whatever you say."

I guess he was too scared of me to refuse.

We each asked our parents for fifty shekels and went to stand in line.

When my turn came, I asked the artist to make it as an exact a copy as he could. I didn't say why because I was afraid he'd tell other kids about my idea. I wanted to be the only one doing it. Shauli's turn came, and he had his mask made. When we both had our masks, I said to him, "Let's go find a mirror and try them on."

As we walked around looking for a mirror, I could sense that Shauli was slowly relaxing and getting used to being with me. We found a sink with a mirror above it and tried on each other's mask.

It was incredible.

We were the same height, and we had the same color eyes. We just stood there looking in the mirror and couldn't get over it.

Still…

I felt that something was missing. Though the masks fit perfectly, if you looked closely you could still see it was a mask.

I had another brilliant idea.

"We'll make a double deception for our friends. We'll both dress up in costumes. Let's say I'll be a policeman and you, Shauli, will be a fireman.

"Usually, in the end, everyone figures out who's wearing the costume. So they'll say to me, 'Ha, ha! We know you're Shauli!' and they'll tell you, 'We know it's you, Gadi.' Their brains will stop right there. They'll never suspect that there's another trick going on. What do you say?"

Shauli was pleased. I don't know whether he was happy about the idea or just the fact that I was letting him be part of my world. We made up that we'd continue to stay distant from one another in class and talk only over the phone.

It was Rosh Chodesh Adar. Only fourteen more days to go.

Every day I called Shauli at home to make plans. I decided that our misleading costumes would be "Haman HaRasha and Mordechai HaYehudi." Shauli agreed. Big deal. He already agreed in advance to everything I said.

"Who do you want to be," I asked him, "Haman or Mordechai?"

"It doesn't matter," he said. "You decide."

I thought about it and decided that I would be Haman and he would be Mordechai. It never crossed my mind that there might be something behind that choice. It revealed that in my heart of hearts I saw quiet, sensitive Shauli as Mordechai, while I, as unpleasant as the thought might be, was more of a Haman.

Purim arrived.

A few days earlier, I went with my mother to buy my Haman costume. She was surprised at my choice, to say the least. She didn't know that it wasn't just a costume but a costume for a costume.

Then came the big day. I coordinated everything with Shauli down to the last detail. I gave him detailed guidelines on how not to be discovered by my best friends. I even gave him a tip that if they asked him why he was so quiet, he should say that he didn't feel well.

I'd thought of everything, or so I assumed. I had no idea what awaited me.

*   *   *

I arrived in class and waited for someone to say something to me. But not a single person spoke to me. I started to hang around my friends, but they walked right past me as if I were invisible.

"What do you think of my costume?" I dared say to one boy.

"Yuck," he sneered. "Too bad you didn't dress up as Vayzata," he said and walked away.

I stood in a corner for a few minutes, and then I heard some excited voices say, "Hey, look—Gadi's coming! Wait till you see his costume."

I watched as my friends surrounded Shauli and started showering him with compliments.

"Wow!"

"What a great costume."

"Awesome."

"We'd never guess it was you."

Shauli tried to pretend to be me, but he couldn't quite pull it off. Luckily, the boys didn't think in that direction.

"Hey, Gadi," one of them said, "how come you're so quiet today?"

Someone else answered, "He wants to be the perfect Mordechai," and everyone laughed as if it was hilarious.

I stuck to them like glue, but except for being elbowed out of the way with someone saying, "Move. Why are you bothering us?" no one paid any attention to me. Everyone was clustered around Shauli, giving him compliments and buttering him up.

When Shauli told them he wasn't feeling well, one boy ran to bring him water while another said, "Maybe get a Tylenol from the secretary."

I stood there and watched everyone hovering over Shauli, thinking how ridiculous it all looked.

During recess, I got some attention from my good friend Moshe, who thought, of course, that he was talking to Shauli.

"Shauli, you dressed up as Haman," he said. "Ha, ha, ha."

Everyone laughed, though I didn't see anything funny about it.

"Too bad you didn't bring Haman's galoshes," my friend Aryeh said. "Didn't you know that Haman had galoshes?"

At first, it didn't bother me all that much because it was all directed at Shauli. But as time went on, the

insults started to get to me. I'd never been in a situation before where someone had mocked me, mimicked me, or laughed at me.

"What's with you guys?" I said to them.

That brought a chorus of, "What's with you guys? Ha, ha, ha. Shauli wants to know what's with us. Ha, ha, ha."

Suddenly I felt a slap on the back and then another one on the shoulder. It hurt, but more than the physical pain was the emotional pain. They were putting me down. I wanted to tear off the costume and shout at them, but I decided I wasn't going to do it. I'd just wait and play the game until the end.

When school ended, I saw them whispering with Shauli. I was jealous. They were making plans, and I wasn't included. I inched my way closer, but Aryeh noticed.

"Hey, Shauli," he said, "why are you sticking your nose into things that are none of your business? Scram."

Plain and simple.

I realized that they were planning on getting together like we did every year, and I felt that I just had to be there, if not to enjoy myself, then at least to know what was going on.

I gathered up my courage and said, "It'll be worth your while to include me. I have something to show you that you've never seen in your life."

Aryeh went back to the group and told them what I'd said. Some just laughed as if Aryeh had told a good joke.

"Shauli, huh? You're sure you're not exaggerating?"

I felt bad for Shauli, who stood with them, listening to it all, but then I remembered that I should really feel bad for myself because right then I was Shauli.

After some discussion, it seemed that they were curious to know what I'd show them.

Meir came over to me and said, "Okay. Come to the shul at three, and we'll leave from there. But don't tell anyone."

I felt good. I'd managed to do what Shauli never could: they'd invited me to go somewhere with them.

I went home and called up Shauli, but he wasn't home. I called again and again, but I couldn't get hold of him. I told myself that he'd probably gone to his aunt's house or something.

At three, I went to the shul and waited.

Ten minutes passed, but no one came. Twenty minutes more went by. Half an hour.

It dawned on me that they'd tricked me.

How stupid could I be? What was I thinking—that they'd include me?

I started to cry. I don't know if I was crying for myself or for Shauli. I'd been Shauli too long to distinguish between the two. But the crying was mine, and the tears were mine.

I remembered that in previous years my friends and I would leave together as soon as school ended. How had I forgotten that? I'd been sitting at home waiting while they were out having fun. How much could a person take? I felt like I just hated them.

That was the moment when I realized how much a few kids in the class were suffering. More than that, I realized that the person who had caused it was none other than yours truly, along with my friends. I realized that the kid they hated was me. And when I remembered how much pain I was in and how much hatred I felt, I started to cry again, because how could I not have seen it all these years.

After I had calmed down, I thought some more, and suddenly I knew exactly where they were right then.

How did I know? Well, wasn't I the one who had always chosen the spot every year? Hadn't I led them all to the park for a barbecue?

I thought about it for another second or two, and then I knew exactly where they'd gone.

I decided to go there.

The park was a few streets past the shul. The closer I got, the surer I became about what I was about to do.

And then I saw them. Some of them were sitting, some were standing, but they were all happy, and they were all trying to impress me—that is, Shauli. And I knew they were all blaming themselves for not quite succeeding.

I walked quickly toward them until Yair spotted me.

"Hey," Yair called out to the group, "he found us. Shauli Galoshes."

The reactions were mixed. Some boys were annoyed; some laughed.

"Are you spying on us?" Aryeh laughed and grabbed my shoulders until I gave a strangled cry.

"Leave the poor guy alone," Yair said scornfully. "He dressed up as Haman like some kid in first grade."

Everyone laughed. I didn't know what hurt more, Aryeh's physical aggression or Yair's mockery.

"*Vayavo Haman*" they started to sing while dancing around me, "wearing rags and big galoshes."

Then Shimi came over and said to me, "Okay,

Shauli. Take those feet of yours and beat it. And don't you ever dare try to spy on us again. Get out of here and say thank you that you got off cheap. You can call it a Purim miracle if you like. Right, Gadi?" he added, turning to Shauli.

"Not right," I heard Shauli say.

"What do you mean?"

"You're just a bunch of mean-spirited kids," I heard Shauli say. "I dressed up as Mordechai, but I really should have dressed up as Haman. You're all little Hamans."

They were in shock. On the one hand, Gadi had just said some very harsh words. On the other hand, it was Gadi, so who could challenge him?

"You are one hundred percent right," I said. "I was blind, but now my eyes have been opened."

None of the kids knew what was going on.

"I'll leave," I said, "but before I do, I want to keep my promise that I would show you something. Remember?"

No one moved.

I stood facing Shauli and said, "At the count of three...

"One.

"Two.

"Three!"

We took off our masks.

I won't even try to describe to you what happened there at that moment.

They stood there facing us, scared stiff. They didn't know what was going on, and when they caught on, they were even more terrified. They couldn't get a word out of their mouths.

I went back to being Gadi.

"I thought I'd found the perfect costume," I told them, "but I discovered that I've been wearing a costume all along.

"In just a few hours I've realized how much I've hurt others, how arrogant and condescending I've been, how much pain I've caused, and how much I've humiliated others. And I had absolutely no idea I was doing it, because I was living in a disguise. I'm so ashamed, so sorry for it. I thank Hashem for giving me the chance to remove that costume and see the truth.

"That's it. It's over. You can forget about whatever was. I'm not blaming anyone, only myself. If you want to join me and go back to being good kids, decent kids, great. If not, I'll go my own way. Come on, Shauli. Let's go. I'd like to make amends for everything I did."

Shauli and I walked away together.

After we'd taken a few steps, I heard a voice call

out, "Wait a minute, Gadi. Don't go. Come talk to us."

I looked at Shauli, and he nodded.

We went back and sat there for a few hours. I spoke a little, and Shauli spoke a lot. Everyone encouraged him to tell what he and his friends had gone through over the years. It made a powerful impression on everyone there, and we all promised to change the way we treated him and the other boys.

A year has gone by since then. Everything in our class has changed. You have no idea how much.

I'll always remember that Purim for letting me see myself—and who I want to be.

I'll always remember the disguise that released me from my own disguise.

The Train of Fear

My name is Leah.

I'm twelve, and I live in Netanya. I'm the oldest of five.
I have two sisters and two brothers.

We're *olim chadashim* from France. *Olim chadashim*
are people who emigrate to Eretz Yisrael from a different
country. We came here five years ago, but we'll probably
be considered new immigrants for another few years.

I could tell you about our adjustment difficulties,
about leaving my old school and all my friends. I could
tell you about my old neighborhood and about France.
Each of those deserves a story of its own.

But none are like the story I'm about to tell you.

I just hope I can capture in words what we went
through on that fateful day.

* * *

Though we made aliyah, we often go back to France to visit our grandparents and other relatives. It's only a short plane ride away.

This past summer when we were in France, my parents decided to take us on a trip to Switzerland. They bought tickets for the TGV train from Paris to Zurich. The trip takes over three hours. In case you don't know, over 600 high-speed trains travel through France each day. The TGV trains travel at speeds of 200 mph. My parents chose a route with scenic views in both France and Switzerland. The train ride itself is an experience because of the luxurious conditions and amenities.

Little did we dream that this trip would turn into a nightmare.

* * *

We waited at the Paris station.

We were seven people in total: my father and mother, my grandparents, me, and my two brothers —seven-year-old Rafael and one-year-old David, who was still in a stroller. My two sisters stayed with my aunt.

We were told that we had thirty seconds to board the train once it pulled into the station.

The train arrived.

Rafael got on first. My father put the stroller, with David in it, onto the train, as well as our two suitcases. He quickly lifted another small bag, and then—

The train doors closed.

My father ran to the train and grabbed the doors to try to keep them from closing, but they closed shut in his face.

I can't describe the panic we felt. I saw Rafael looking at us. I don't think he realized yet the full extent of what had just happened, but he looked shocked.

My father banged on the door and shouted to Rafael, "Get off at the next stop! Do you hear me?"

He didn't hear him.

The train started to move

I ran alongside the train, banging on the door in despair, and shouted again, "Get off at the next stop, you hear?"

Rafael still looked frightened but nodded.

The train pulled out of the station.

My mother was hysterical. My grandparents were speechless.

* * *

We ran to the main office, but the people there

didn't seem too excited. All they said was, "Take the next train."

We found out that the amount of time the doors stayed open at that station wasn't thirty seconds but *fifteen* seconds, and that's where we'd made our mistake.

"Where's the next station?" my mother asked.

"Half an hour away," came the answer.

"And the station after that?" my father asked.

The station after that was three hours away, deep in Switzerland.

We ran back to the platform so that we wouldn't miss the next train. My thoughts raced. I pictured seven-year-old Rafael standing on the train near the stroller with David and two suitcases bigger than both of them.

In my mind's eye, I could see him standing there, scared stiff, almost too afraid to breathe. Would he remember to get off at the next station in a half hour?

* * *

When the next train pulled into the station, we boarded, and so began the longest half hour in my life.

We kept looking at our watches, waiting for one thing only: to arrive at the next station.

We didn't know what to plan. Should we get off at the next stop no matter what? Or should we first check the platform to see if Rafael and David were there?

We knew that when we reached the station, we'd have only thirty seconds to decide what to do: whether to get off or to continue to the next stop.

After a nerve-racking half hour, the train slowed down and approached the platform. Hearts pounding, we stood watching, each of us at a different window, to see if would spot Rafael and David.

The station was empty!

Suddenly, my grandmother cried out, "There are the suitcases!"

We breathed a sigh of relief. Rafael must have heard Abba's shouted instructions, and he'd gotten off.

The train pulled in slowly and stopped right next to the suitcases. And then a terrible realization dawned on us.

Two suitcases were there, all right—
But not Rafael and David!

*   *   *

The doors opened.

Five seconds of panic—and another twenty-five seconds to decide what to do.

My father got off the train and started shouting, "Rafael! Rafael!"

No one answered.

He returned to the train. We looked at him helplessly.

And then he said, "Listen, we have to divide up. Let Saba and Savta stay here," he suggested to my grandparents, "because maybe the children did get off at this station. We'll continue to the next station. Maybe Rafael was able to get the two suitcases off but didn't have enough time to get the stroller off before the train began moving."

We had five seconds to decide.

My father's idea seemed like the best option in the terrible situation we were in.

Saba and Savta quickly got off the train. The doors closed, and my parents and I began a journey of three hours, a journey in search of a helpless seven-year-old boy with a toddler in a stroller. We all knew what Rafael and David were going through, but we had no way to help them.

My parents called the train's management.

In France, everything is complicated. It took us half an hour to get a live person on the line instead of an automated answer, but even then, we were told that they had no way of knowing what was taking place on the train.

My parents' request that they stop the train Rafael and David were on drew a sharp refusal.

My parents decided to sit and do what all Jewish parents do when faced with trouble: to daven to Hashem.

The three of us began saying *Tehillim*. (My mother had a small *sefer Tehillim* in her purse. I said *Tehillim* along with her, and my father said it by heart.)

Tears filled our eyes.

People around us stared at us in surprise, wondering what had happened to us and why we were crying, but no one offered any help.

Suddenly my mother said that she wanted to make a resolution. If everything turned out okay, *b'ezras Hashem*, we'd all go to Kever Rochel and light a candle there.

"Why there specifically?" my father asked, because usually, we go to the *kever* of Rabi Shimon bar Yochai and Rabi Meir Baal HaNes.

My mother sobbed softly, then wiped her eyes and whispered the words: *"Kol b'ramah nishmah*, A voice is heard on high, wailing, bitter weeping. Rochel weeps for her children. She refuses to be consoled for her children, for they are gone."

When she said that, all three of us burst out crying. That was exactly our situation. I think I forgot to tell you that my mother's name is Rochel. And now, like Rochel Imeinu, she was weeping for her children because they were gone.

During those moments of sheer terror, we couldn't do anything but cry so hard we couldn't stop.

* * *

Eventually, one of the passengers came over and gently asked if everything was all right.

We told her what had happened, and she ran to her husband and told him the story. Soon a crowd gathered, everyone wanting to help.

But aside from offering advice, not much could be done much.

Several people took out their cell phones, but they soon came to the same conclusion we had. There really wasn't anything that could be done.

We continued saying *Tehillim*. My father explained to our new train friends, in French, of course, that my mother held a book of Psalms that Jews call *Tehillim*. It turns out that many of them were familiar with many of the Psalms and several began to murmur verses as well. It was a strange scene.

That's how we passed the three of the longest hours of our lives.

During the last fifteen minutes, our nerves reached a breaking point as we waited tensely to see what would happen when the train pulled into the station.

I pictured two different scenarios: One, the train pulls into the station, and there's a baby in a stroller with a boy standing near it. We rush over to the children and hug them with all our might.

The second is different. I picture an empty station or a station full of people, but no boy or stroller in sight.

The train pulled into the station, and what do you think we saw?

Neither a boy nor a stroller. Nothing.

* * *

We were in total shock. What now? Who should we ask?

Within minutes, the platform had cleared. The masses of people who had gotten off the train were gone.

This might surprise you, but at least half of the people who were in our car and who knew our story refused to leave without first trying to help us find the children.

My mother and I burst into tears again. All the women who got off the train with us came over to console us. The men gathered around my father silently.

In the midst of this chaos, a policeman came up to us and said, "Is there a Monsieur_____ here?" saying my father's name.

"That's me," my father said, surprised to hear his name called.

"Come with me," the policeman said and began walking away.

We all followed him: my father, my mother, and I, and all the people who were with us on the train.

My father asked the policeman in French, "What's going on?" but the policeman said in English that he didn't speak French that well, only Swiss-German. He told us, in English, to follow him.

The people near me began to ask him about the children, but he was tough. All he would say was, "Just come with me."

That scared us. Why wasn't he willing to talk to us? What did he have to hide? Where exactly was he taking us?

What had happened to Rafael and David?

We went down two levels and stepped on a moving sidewalk. The group from our train car was still with us. I guess they felt that they had to know what had become of the lost children.

We went up a level and reached a new platform.

The first thing we saw was...

A policewoman.

And next to her...a seven-year-old boy alongside a stroller holding a one-year-old child.

Rafael and David!

* * *

I don't think the three of us ever ran as fast as we did right then.

Rafael saw us first and shouted "Ima!" but he didn't run toward us. Later we figured out that he hadn't wanted to leave the stroller even for a second.

We reached him and hugged him and David tightly. Now my mother's weeping—Rochel crying over her children who were gone—turned into tears of joy. She was rewarded for her prayers, and her sons returned.

All the other passengers who had cried along with us now wanted to pat Rafael on the head and tell him what a brave and responsible boy he was. Some of them offered him candy (that wasn't kosher), and two people even put money in his pocket. They wanted to show solidarity with us. They, too, were part of the story.

My father asked the policewoman how the children came there, and she said that several passengers who had gotten off the train had reported a child and a baby who had been forgotten on the train. The police talked to the boy, who told them that his family was visiting France and that when they got separated, his father had shouted to him to wait at the next station (the one before this one). The policewoman said that Rafael told her that he wanted to go back to the previous station because that's where his family was waiting.

"I offered to send him back with one of the policemen," she told us. "I said I'd wait here because maybe they'd get off at this station. But he refused to go with the policeman. He said that his parents allowed him to go only with a woman." (My mother had read him the book *What Should You Do Now?* which has a story about a girl who is lost. It says that if a child gets lost, he should ask a woman, not a man, for help. Rafael was following those instructions.)

"The policeman stayed on the platform, and he's the one who brought you here. I took your son to the other platform, the one for the return train. I was going to take him back on that three-hour trip because he insisted that you were waiting for him there. Now you've saved me the trip," she said. Then she added,

"You have a very smart son. You're Jews, aren't you?"

*   *   *

We thanked the policewoman profusely. My father called my grandparents, who were waiting with the suitcases, to tell them that we had found Rafael and David. He said they should board the next train coming our way, with the suitcases, and meet us here.

*   *   *

At the end of all the hugs and kisses, we calmed down. My parents said there were still a few questions left—for example, how did the suitcases get to the platform, but not Rafael? They waited for Rafael to feel relaxed enough to talk and then they asked him to tell us the story. Here's what he said.

"You shouted at me to get off at the next station," Rafael said, "and the train started to go, and I cried but quietly so David wouldn't hear me and get scared, but he did, and he started to cry too. Then I told him that you were waiting at the next stop. I didn't know where the next stop was or how long it would take to get there, but I was ready for it.

"After we had traveled for a while I suddenly realized that I'd have to get the suitcases off the train, too. They're

big and heavy, and I didn't know how I'd do it. I decided to push them off first, and then get off with David.

"After a while, the train pulled into the station, and I pushed the suitcases off. It was easy because of the wheels. Then I got off with David.

"But after I got off," Rafael said, "I suddenly realized that the platform was completely empty except for one person who got off with us. I thought a little, and I said to myself that if I asked you, you wouldn't allow me to be there alone in a strange place with a stranger who could do something to us.

"Then the man began to walk in our direction.

"I didn't think too much," Rafael said. "I ran back to the train, and a second before the door closed, I pushed the stroller on and got on it again. The suitcases stayed on the platform, and the train continued on its way.

"At first, I thought you might be mad at me, but then I told myself that you'd understand why I got back on the train."

Abba hugged Rafael hard and said to him, "You're so smart! That's just what your mother and I would have wanted you to do."

Rafael had more to say.

"The train kept on going. In the beginning, I just

stood there. But then I started crying, and David started yelling, 'Ima! Ima!' until one of the passengers came and asked what had happened, so I told her.

"People started talking all at once, and then one of the passengers called the managers of the train. When we got here a few hours later, two policemen were waiting for us.

"I told them that you were waiting for us at the stop before this one. I told them what had happened, and then they talked it over and said that one of them could take me back to that stop. But I told them that I wouldn't go with a policeman, just with a policewoman. They laughed and said that the policewoman could take David and me here. We waited for the train, and after half an hour you came. That's it."

*　*　*

I always knew my brother Rafael was smart, but I hadn't known just how smart. Hashem had blessed him with intelligence, resourcefulness, and the ability to stay calm under pressure, all of which gave our story a happy ending.

The crowd from the train couldn't get over Rafael's story. One of them said, "Jews are a wise people, isn't that so?"

We said goodbye warmly and thanked them for their support. We'd become brothers in a sense. It was a real *kiddush Hashem*.

My father and mother will keep their vow and go up to Rochel's Tomb to daven, and they're taking us four children along too. We'll weep bitterly for Rochel Imeinu, who surely cried for our children when they were gone, and in whose merit and in the merit of her tears, my parents' children—my brothers—were returned to their borders.

Bike Mystery

My name is Matis.

I'm twelve years old, and I live near Yerushalayim.

I'm a friendly, popular kid who likes to play and do stuff—especially ride my bike. My teachers always tell my father that I've got great potential and a good understanding of the material, but that I often daydream in class.

After the last PTA meeting, my father declared that if during the next semester I paid attention in class the way I was supposed to, he'd buy me a special bike.

From that day on, I started to do two things: One, I started to learn, and, two, I started to dream about the bike he'd promised me—not during class, though, because then I'd only be able to dream about it and not actually get it!

The results were as expected: within a month my grades had gone from one extreme to the other.

I must admit that the change alone brought me a lot of satisfaction and happiness, which was a prize in and of itself. In the beginning, I paid attention *shelo lishmah*—meaning, I was doing it for the reward of the bicycle. But then later I noticed that I was enjoying the learning itself, so I kept on paying attention *lishmah*.

*   *   *

After Tisha B'Av I went with my father to a major bicycle store.

I left there with a bike that I'd never dreamed I'd own. It cost more than any other bike I'd ever owned, lost, broken, or had stolen from me, combined.

As soon as I got home, I started to ride the bike and enjoy all its new features. I made sure to tell my parents that even though I already had the bike, I would continue to pay attention in class.

Every kid who owns a bike gets plenty of requests from kids who want to ride it around the block. A kid with a bike like mine gets double and triple the number of requests because everyone wants to try it out.

In the past, I would let kids ride my bike from time to time. But when I got the new bike, so many kids asked me to ride it that I had to refuse too many kids too many times.

It's only natural that when you refuse to let a kid take your bike for a spin around the block, his feelings are hurt, and he won't exactly like the boy who refused him.

* * *

One day, my father sent me to the post office.

I was only too happy to volunteer. I took the package, strapped it to the back of the bike, put on my helmet, and set out for the post office branch closest to our house.

When we'd bought the bike, the store had offered several different types of helmets. My father bought me the most expensive one, the one I had asked for.

Next came the chain. They'd had a big selection of chains with a wide range of prices. I chose the least expensive one.

I'm telling you this for a reason; soon you'll see why.

When I got to the post office, I parked the bike at the bike stand outside. Then I wrapped the chain around the bike and the stand, locked it, and went inside.

Inside the post office was the usual long line. I waited a while until my turn finally came. I mailed the package for my father and rushed back outside to my bike.

When I got to the bike stand, I discovered to my shock…

No. Not what you're thinking.

My bike was there, but it was chained to the stand with two chains. One, the cheap one, was mine, which I opened with the small key I had (which probably fit every single chain like that…).

But my bike was locked with an additional chain, a very thick one.

I tried to open the lock but quickly realized it was impossible. The chain was made of steel, and even with the help of a few metal rods, it was impossible to break.

Strange. Why would someone want to lock my bike?

And the most important question of all: What was I going to do now?

* * *

A few kids noticed my problem. They tried to help me break the lock, but they too realized it couldn't be done. One of them suggested breaking the bike

stand, but I said to him, "What's the matter with you? It doesn't belong to us." Everyone burst out laughing, and I realized that he hadn't meant it seriously. But I was too tense to laugh right then.

With no other choice, I walked home. When I got there, I told my father what had happened. He went with me to the post office and tried to release my bicycle, but he didn't succeed. In the end, he called a locksmith. The locksmith arrived and in two minutes managed to break open the lock.

* * *

Now I was left with the question of what to do with the chain.

After thinking it over, my father said we should take the chain home with us and put up signs in the neighborhood announcing that we had it. That way, the person who locked the chain around my bicycle— whether as a prank or for some other reason—could call us and get back the chain and maybe even explain why he'd done it.

A few days went by. I told the story of the bike chain to my friends, and we all discussed why we thought the owner of the chain did what he did. Had he wanted to lock my bike and then come back later to take it? Or maybe he'd been jealous and hadn't wanted me to ride the bike.

Most of the kids thought the second suggestion made the most sense.

One morning, a boy came into class and announced, "I discovered who locked up your bike! It's Nati, from fifth grade."

"Nati?" I said. "I remember he asked me a couple of times if he could ride my bike, and I said no. I guess he wanted to get back at me."

*   *   *

Without giving it too much thought, a few of us kids went down to Nati's fifth-grade classroom to teach him a lesson.

It was nearly the end of recess, so most of the kids were back in the classroom. "Where's Nati?" I asked, ready for battle.

Nati walked up to me.

"Did you by any chance lose a chain?" I said sarcastically.

"Yes!" Nati exclaimed. "Did you find it?"

"You could say that," I said, trying to figure out if he really didn't know what was going on or if he was faking it and making fun of me.

"Where is it?" he asked.

"Before you ask where it is, maybe you want to tell me where you lost it."

"I can tell you exactly where. It was next to the bike rack at the post office on 5 Derech Kedem. It's a very expensive red chain, and I—"

"You don't need to continue," I cut him off. "Do you mind telling me why you chained my bike? You had nothing better to do, right?"

Nati was shocked speechless. He opened his mouth to talk and then closed it. Then he said, "You mean to say it was your bike?"

"Yes, it was my bike, the same bike you asked to ride and I refused to let you. Very interesting how you suddenly recognized it. Let's say the bike belonged to someone else. Can you please explain to me why a normal kid would chain someone else's bike, making him stuck for a couple of hours?"

* * *

Nati started to cry. A friend of Nati's came up to me and said, "I was with him, and I know why he put a chain on your bike."

"Very nice," I said, my voice dripping with venom. "So, there's a partner to the crime. '*Oy larasha, v'oy*

lischeno. Woe to the evildoer and woe to his neighbor.'"

"You might want to listen to the story first and then decide if any crime was committed," the boy said.

"We were both riding our bikes down the street near the post office," he continued, "when suddenly we saw two older boys we'd never seen before playing around with the lock on your bike.

"'Look at that,' Nati said to me. 'They're trying to steal that expensive bike. There's a boy in our school who has a bike like that.'

"'But who chains an expensive bike like that with such a cheap chain?' we wondered. We stopped and tried to think of a plan. On the one hand, we wanted to stop them from stealing the bike. At the same time, though, we were afraid of them.

"Then Nati said, 'Take my bike and hide.'

"He went over to the bike with his chain and bravely pretended not to notice the other boys. He bent over the bicycle as if it belonged to him and wrapped his chain around the frame, the wheel, and the bike rack, locked it, and walked away.

"You'd better believe it that in another minute they would have gotten your chain off and you would have lost your bicycle!" the boy said.

"We went back there a few hours later and

discovered that the bike was gone—along with the chain. We thought that maybe those boys had stolen it after all, despite everything we'd done."

* * *

I'd never felt so uncomfortable. Thanks to Nati, my bike wasn't stolen, yet I'd thought the worst things about him.

I went over to him and said, embarrassed, "I'm really sorry. I never imagined such a story. You're a smart, caring boy. You saved my bike, and instead of thanking you, I got mad at you. Do you forgive me?"

Nati nodded, and we left the classroom. Within minutes, word of Nati's quick thinking spread through the school. People were talking about his brilliant idea for a long time after that.

Since then, I've become good friends with Nati. And just so it's clear, ever since he gets as many rides on my bike as he wants. He deserves it. For sure. He forgave me for lashing out at him like that, and I learned something important: to judge everyone favorably and to hold myself back before bursting out at someone.

At least that lock taught me a great lesson—to lock my lips!

Groups at War

My name is Orit.

I'm thirteen years old, and I live in Petach Tikvah.

I think my story will interest a lot of girls who came up against the same issue I did or who might in the future.

I'm not exactly what you'd call a quiet girl, but I'm also not loud. I'm not a leader or anything, but I fit in very well with the group. I have a friend named Tehilla who's just like me: a regular, nice, good girl, maybe a little more noticeable. We've been good friends since preschool.

As you might expect, we were part of a group of girls in our class (yet we still were friends with the rest of the girls).

I want to write a few words about groups.

In practically every class there are several groups of girls who have things in common. There are groups that keep to themselves and separate themselves from the rest of their classmates. This causes jealousy and hard feelings. And there are groups that get along well with all the girls and don't make a point of keeping to themselves.

In our class, we had a group of girls who kept their distance. They did it on purpose to create a kind of "us-against-them" mentality. Everything they said became a "secret," and every gathering at someone's house became a "secret that everyone knew about but didn't know about." I'm sure you know what I'm talking about. They wanted to give their meetings an aura of secrecy, yet they wanted everyone to know that they had a secret no one else knew.

This caused a lot of jealousy and animosity. Girls who wanted to become part of their group were heartbroken when they were rejected. They called the girls in the group "snobs" and were angry with them, but the girls in the group didn't care. Maybe they even liked it. They enjoyed being the center of attention.

Our group always had an excellent relationship with the rest of the girls. We didn't feel like it was urgent for us to emphasize an "us-against-them" mentality, and the girls in our group were easygoing and had good *middos*, so everything went along calmly and peacefully.

* * *

One day, Tehilla, who was in our group, started becoming friendly with Shira, who belonged to the group of "snobs." Their friendship seemed strange to us, but we didn't say anything about it.

One day, Tehilla suggested that we include Shira in the *oneg Shabbos* we were having that week. Reluctantly, we agreed. Because we didn't want to be a "closed group," we sometimes did include other girls. In principle, we had nothing against it.

We had no idea what we were getting into.

If you know how things work, then you know that by Sunday every single girl in class knew that Shira came to our group's *oneg Shabbos*. I think the one who leaked the information was a girl in the group who wanted to boast. Girls in the "snob" group were up in arms over it and put Shira in *"cherem"* for daring to "humiliate the group by participating in activities of another group."

Seeing that Shira was a little sad about it, a few girls in our group said to her, "Forget about them. What do you need them for? Join us."

And that's what happened.

We didn't know what we were getting into.

From that day on, the competition between our group and the snobs was fierce. I'm ashamed to tell you how far it went: anonymous letters, *lashon hara*, *rechilus*, conspiracies, and quarrels. Girls in the snob group made sure to spread the rumor that they had kicked Shira out of their group. They said they couldn't stand her to begin with. Shira didn't hold back, either. She said all kinds of things about the girls in the group and even revealed group secrets. That caused an earthquake. It was like they were state secrets or something.

*   *   *

Actually, all of us got caught up in it. We'd wake up with it the morning and go to sleep with it at night. The competition filled our minds with stories of petty intrigues about the other group and anger at the stories they spread about us. The classroom became a battleground of *lashon hara* and *rechilus*, with tons of anger and *sinas chinam* in the air.

Without our being aware of it, our group became just like the other group. We had secrets that were zealously guarded so they wouldn't leak—but of course did leak. We had strict rules about who you could talk to and who you couldn't, with "categories" and jealousy.

We weren't even aware that it was happening.

The first time I realized something was off was when I walked down the block near my house and met my classmate Rachel. I said hello and began a conversation with her.

She looked uncomfortable. She stammered, and I could see she was nervous.

"Rachel," I asked her, "did something happen?"

"I don't know," she said. "I'm just surprised you're talking to me."

"Huh?" I said. "Why shouldn't I talk to you."

"I don't know," she said. "Suddenly you've become a group of..." She searched for the right word and then said, "snobs."

"Our group? Snobs?" I almost shouted. "What are you talking about? You're making a big mistake. How can you compare us to...?"

"I didn't think so before," Rachel said. "Before you weren't, but now you are."

We talked a few minutes more and then went our separate ways.

I couldn't stop thinking about what she'd said. I called

Tehilla and told her about my encounter with Rachel.

"Well, what did you think?" Tehilla said to me. "Of course that's how they see us. This is news to you?"

Tehilla told me she'd noticed this from the start and had promised herself not to be like that. That's why she was still talking to most of the girls in class. "But sort of in secret, so that none of the girls in the group will get mad."

"Hold on," I said. "Are you telling me, Tehilla, that you hid your relationship with other girls from me?"

"Yes," Tehilla admitted. "I was sure you'd be against it."

"Let's say that I would," I said. "Still, I thought we were friends who didn't hide things from each other, certainly not something as simple as a relationship with other girls."

That's what I said, and then I hung up. I was mad, and I wanted her to know it.

*   *   *

Several days passed. A girl in the group had a birthday party, and the next day news of the party "leaked" to the rest of the class.

Shira (the new member of our group who came from the other group, in case you forgot) was the first to suspect Tehilla as being the one who leaked the secret. "I saw her talking with a few girls. She's not sticking with the group."

This accusation spread quickly from girl to girl, and within minutes everyone was against Tehilla.

Tehilla found out about it in a very original way. She went over to talk to a girl in the group, and the girl said to her scornfully, "Wouldn't it be a shame for me to say something that will just go straight to others? I'd rather talk to them directly."

Tehilla tried to understand what was going on but ran into a brick wall. She realized that she was being excluded from our group.

Her face fell. She didn't even come over to talk to me.

I didn't understand why. If she had, I would have talked with her. But because she didn't try to talk to me, I got even more upset at her.

A few days went by like this. Tehilla looked despondent. Suddenly she'd been cast out of the group and separated from her BFF — me.

I cared. I waited for her to come talk to me, but she never did.

I told the other girls in the group that we shouldn't be so hard on Tehilla, but they all said, "It's about time we put a stop to the leaks by letting girls know there are serious consequences."

I didn't know what to do. My friendship with Tehilla had been cut off in one miserable moment—and I missed it. Still, I realized that if I sided with her, I might also be put in *cherem*. I definitely did not want that! Just the possibility of it scared me to death.

After a week and a half of this, I couldn't keep it in anymore. I decided to talk to my father.

My father is someone people talk to about social issues. He understands these things and always has good ideas about how to get out of trouble—and how to avoid getting into trouble in the first place.

I told him what was going on.

"You know our family rules," my father said. "We don't commit injustices, and we don't let other people commit injustices against us. We don't get into petty arguments, and if someone gets into a disagreement with us, we try to make peace with him.

"And another thing," he said. "We're also loyal to our friends."

"I know that, Abba," I said, "but this is complicated. Tehilla is the one who stopped talking to me. And besides, if I go back to being friends with her now, I'll be kicked out of the group, and I think I'd be devastated if that happened."

"Look, Orit," my father said after thinking about it

a little, "I understand the sensitive position you're in. I also want things to be good for my daughter. I want her to be surrounded by friends. But your mother and I raised you with values. That's why I'm saying what I'm saying. I won't force you to resume contact with Tehilla, and I won't be angry with you if you decide it's too much for you to handle. I'm just telling you the right thing to do.

"And I want to tell you that I personally have stood at a few crossroads like that in my life. I acted according to what my conscience told me. I paid the price, just as you will if you decide to follow the path in which we raised you. But one thing is clear. In the end, I didn't lose out at all. Look how many true friends I have, people who are willing to sacrifice for me the same way I sacrificed for them.

"And another thing," my father said. "I can promise you that your mother and I will stand behind you and support you if your decision causes any problems."

I didn't need that promise. My parents always stand behind me and support me.

That very same day I went to Tehilla's house and asked to speak with her.

She was surprised…and a little angry.

"How nice of you to come down from your ivory

tower to speak with simple folk like me," she said cynically.

"Huh?" I said. "Who stopped talking to the other person? Not me."

"Of course it was you!" Tehilla said. "You went around telling everyone what I had told you, that I talk with girls outside the group."

"Why are you saying something like that?" I said, upset.

"Because if it wasn't you, then how did they know?"

"I have no idea," I said, "but how can you even think I would do something like that? That's how well you know me? Was there ever a time when I wasn't loyal to you?"

"Wait a minute. Are you trying to say that you didn't tell anyone?"

"I promise you I didn't."

"Then I'm sorry I didn't judge you favorably."

There were a few minutes of tears and apologies, and then we both said, "What do we do now?"

I told her about my little talk with my father and said that I was determined to continue our friendship no matter what. We agreed that we would go forward together.

From there I went to other friends in the group and told them about my decision. I told them that Tehilla hadn't told anyone about the birthday party and that I was against all the snobbiness of not talking with anyone.

As I had expected, a few girls in the group started to put me down, mainly Shira. Most of the girls were scared and kept quiet. When the dust settled, I found myself excluded from the group I had been so much a part of.

To my credit, I can say that it didn't come as a huge surprise.

*   *   *

The following days were hard. Tehilla and I were the targets of slander from our own group, while the rest of the girls in class gloated over our predicament. It was a good thing we had each other. We went through some rough days, but at least we were together.

As the days went by, we connected with more and more girls until we found ourselves part of a very large group—that included most of the girls in class.

I won't try to say that it wasn't hard for me. I missed feeling "being special," being part of a select group of girls that were somehow "better" than the others.

But now we realized how much heartache, anger, and grudges that feeling causes.

We also knew how tense it was for the girls in the two groups (which were really controlled by one or two girls) because they had to adhere to all sorts of strange, complicated rules and regulations.

Six months went by like that. I don't think I'll ever forget that half year. I also don't think I've managed to convey to you the suffering and pain I went through during that time, the fears and the worries. Yet during that time I built something within me that I think will never be destroyed: loyalty, knowing how to be a good friend, and the ability to cope with difficulties. I'm quoting a lot from my father, but I feel that it's part of me.

*   *   *

You're probably curious to know how the story ended.

It happened suddenly. One day, Shira was seen going around with the "snob" group. They all looked pleased as punch.

On the other hand, the girls in our group (our former group) walked around looking totally depressed.

It took us a while to catch on to what had happened.

It had all been a game. Shira's supposed falling out with the "snob" group was staged so that she could become part of our group and report back about what was going on.

It turns out that Shira was the one who leaked the story of the birthday party and everything else that happened in the group. She was finally discovered when a note she'd written to her friend in the "snobs" was discovered.

I know it sounds childish, but for us, it was as big as the story of Russia spying on the United States. Each person and his world. Adults spy to conquer territory and win wars, and girls spy for social status.

Girls in the group came over to Tehilla and me to apologize. We forgave them.

Then they invited us back into the group.

We didn't hesitate for a minute. How could we accept such an offer?

So that's it. We declined. We said, "We suggest that you join our group, which includes all the girls in class. It's about time we drop all this foolish childishness and start being mature."

It took them a few days, but eventually, they agreed.

Another month went by before the snob group

broke off completely. That's what happens when a group doesn't consist of real friends but just people interested in advancing their own agenda.

Now we're one big happy class, and I'm so happy I heeded my father's suggestion. True, I suffered a bit, but what I gained was so much more. It was well worth it.

A Bas Mitzvah to Remember

My name is Rachelli.

I'm twelve and a half, and I live in New York.

I want to tell you about my bas mitzvah party that took place six months ago, but first, let me tell you a little bit about myself. I'm going to tell it straight even though some of what I'm about to say isn't very complimentary to myself.

I live in a very exclusive neighborhood in New York. Ever since I can remember, me and my friends in the neighborhood have been called "JAPs." (In case you don't know, that stands for Jewish American Princess.)

Did it bother us? The truth? We kind of liked it. Uh, more than kind of. Like, very.

Because that's what we were. I've got to admit that I've always been a snob. I held myself in high regard and didn't talk to just *anyone.* I viewed girls who came from the lesser neighborhoods as peasants. I was proud of my parents' wealth—not that it has any real value to be proud of and not that I'd earned it myself.

Not only hadn't I earned it, but I'd never done anything in my life except enjoy the riches my parents showered on me.

I had never in my life cleaned my room, washed a dish, ironed a blouse, or done any grocery shopping. I mean, that's what Joselyn, our live-in, was for, right? She did all that kind of stuff.

Every so often my mother would say to me, "Why don't you straighten up your room?" and I'd give her a look that said, "You're kidding, right?" Or worse, I'd give her a hurt look full of accusation, as if to say, "Why can't you leave a poor child alone?"

You get the picture. And if you do, you know I was pretty *chutzpahdik.* I gave myself free rein to talk to my parents like no girl talks to her parents, except, of course, for a few of my friends. (Not that all the girls in the neighborhood were like that. We felt sorry for the ones who weren't, and they felt sorry for themselves, too.)

I might have continued growing up like that—and who knows what kind of a girl and woman I would have become?

Notice my use of the past tense.

It's because something happened.

And what happened was my bas mitzvah.

*   *   *

Like most of my classmates, I'd been dreaming of my bas mitzvah since I was ten. Okay, so I'm exaggerating. But not by a lot. It was more like eleven.

The subject of our bas mitzvah parties preoccupied us. And just so you understand, we weren't talking about some simple, modest celebration, but exactly the opposite.

We weren't really dreaming about a bas mitzvah party but about a "competition called bas mitzvah." Every girl put her parents into a frenetic race to arrange a there's-never-been-and-never-will-be-another-one-like-it event. The only question was not how much money the parents had, but how much pressure could be put on them to spend.

A few of my friends had very fancy bas mitzvahs with a hall, a theme, an orchestra, and all kinds of entertainers. Each girl claimed that hers was *the* event. Which naturally caused a lot of arguing and fights and tons of jealousy, stress, and pressure.

I began doing the groundwork with my parents to

make sure I'd get the outstanding bas mitzvah of my dreams. Since my parents always wanted to make me happy, they started running around to different party planners to see which one could give me what I wanted.

The problem was, I myself didn't know what I wanted.

Every party planner seemed out of touch, and every program looked babyish. People came and went, and I started feeling like everything was going against me and that my parents weren't trying hard enough.

My parents hinted that no one would want to work with a spoiled little girl who said no to every suggestion.

As soon as they said that I burst into tears and made a scene about how they'd hurt my feelings, and what a poor thing I was. I wasn't just pretending to cry, either. I really felt like I was the most miserable girl in the world. Maybe you're laughing, but that's how spoiled boys and girls feel.

My parents got very upset. But instead of putting me in my place, they started apologizing as if they were the ones who'd done something bad to me and not me to them. They promised me that they'd do some more homework and try to plan for me the very best bas mitzvah possible.

A few days passed. My parents whispered a lot so

I wouldn't hear what they were saying. One day, when they didn't notice me, I overheard them whispering about a certain party planner they'd met. I recognized the name. She wasn't really a party planner but an event planner. She did huge events for thousands of attendees. I caught from my parents' whispers that she'd barely agreed to meet them because doing a bas mitzvah was *so* not on her level. But they had a lot of connections, and they put pressure on her until she agreed to meet them. Somehow, they'd gotten her to agree to do my bas mitzvah, but the price she was asking was sky high and way out of the ballpark for this type of thing.

I couldn't keep quiet (yeah, self-control is definitely one of my problems). "Abba, Mommy, I want her! Even if she costs way more money!"

"Where did you come from?" my parents said, looking at me in shock.

"I was here when suddenly you both began to talk. But now that I heard, I'm not giving in. I don't want anyone but her."

The thought that my parents wouldn't agree never even crossed my mind. I was used to getting my way.

And I did.

* * *

The meeting with the event planner took place in her luxurious office.

My parents told her what they wanted, and she gave them a few ideas. At first, I listened because she was new. But once I got used to her I started to act the same way I'd always acted. I rejected one idea after another, and frowned when she mentioned possible entertainers. At the end, I made a face and said to her, "How pathetic."

No sooner had the words left my mouth when she jumped up and said, "All three of you please get up and leave this office and don't ever come back."

We were in shock. No one had ever talked that way to my parents. My father is a well-known figure with lots of connections. To say something like that to him was like saying it to the president.

I saw that my father was speechless. I'd never seen him that way. Ever. He was always in command and self-assured. Nothing fazed him. But now? He couldn't get a word out of his mouth.

"Did you hear me?" she said. "Get up and don't dump your problem kid on me. Let her drive you crazy, not me."

"How can you talk that way about my daughter?" my mother said.

"In my office, I'll talk however I want," she said. "Not only that, but I know you think exactly the same. I've done my research. All of New York knows that no one wanted to work with you because of your spoiled brat of a daughter, so you decided to try dumping her on me. Cope with it yourselves."

My father was white. My mother started to cry. I did too.

I guess that softened her because she looked at me and said, "I'm talking to you for the last time. If you want a bas mitzvah party the way it should be, then you'll have to listen to me and not give me any instructions. If not, leave the office and find someone else to plan it for you."

*　*　*

I thought fast. I wasn't so much thinking about myself as about my parents. They'd been hugely embarrassed, and I told myself that no way would I let this person humiliate my father and mother, who had stood up for me. I decided to take the humiliation on myself and just give in.

"Okay," I heard myself say. "I apologize. I'll do what you say."

My parents looked at me in astonishment. They'd never heard the word *apologize* come out of my mouth before. (If they'd have caught the tone I'd said it in, they would have realized that it wasn't really an apology but sort of a defiant statement as if to say, "If that's what will make you happy." But the tone I used was more of a code known only to girls my age.)

The event planner gave me a long, hard look. She did understand that tone of voice. She didn't miss a thing! I saw that she was thinking it over, and then she said, "Okay. I don't put too much hope in your apology, but the promise will be enough. From this moment on you're working with me, and together we'll plan your bas mitzvah."

She opened up a planner and said, "You'll come here in two days at two o'clock. Come alone. Let your parents get on with their lives. We'll manage by ourselves."

I looked at my parents, and they looked at me, and then I said, "Got it.

We drove home in total silence. I think my parents felt uncomfortable about what had happened, but I didn't. I felt that she was the best one to produce my bas mitzvah. Weird. I was really mad at her, but I also felt a kind of security.

Two days later I met with her.

She said that she'd understood from my parents that I wanted a party program that no one had ever done before. In order to give me that, she had to know about me and about my friends.

She asked me lots of questions about myself and my friendships. I don't know how she did it, but she managed to discover that I was under a lot of stress and that I didn't trust even my very best friends. I don't know how we got to all those topics, but we did.

Then she said to me, "I think we need to do an event that no one has ever done before. We need to bring people into a world they don't know. Let it sit on me for a day or two, and I'll bring you an amazing theme."

I left her office feeling confident. She didn't get mad at me (probably because I was a little scared of her), and also because we'd had a conversation that left me feeling that she understood me and knew who I really was.

We met two days later. Before we started, she told me that something had just come up. She needed to make an urgent trip to the hospital. She asked me if I wanted to postpone our meeting or if I wanted to come with her.

"I'll come with you," I said.

As we drove to the hospital, she told me that she was a volunteer who distributed balloons to sick kids.

I told her I found it hard to imagine her giving out balloons.

"Why?" she asked me.

"You're such a tough woman. I can't see you blowing up balloons for kids."

"You'd be surprised," she said. "When you get there, you'll see that it's hard to be tough."

When we got to the children's ward, I realized what she was talking about. There were boys and girls of all ages, some bald, some with tubes in their nose or mouth, some with IVs.

I was in shock.

Ranana—that's her name—took out some balloons and started blowing them up. Then she twisted them into all kinds of amazing shapes.

It was like she was a different person from the one I'd known. The kids surrounded her, and I saw that they all knew her really well and adored her. All traces of the tough woman I knew had vanished. It was almost scary.

Somehow, I found myself helping her.

"Tie this balloon," she said to me. "Meanwhile I'll work on the next one. Now hold these two together while I tie them to the third." I turned into a balloon artist, and I must admit I was enjoying every minute of it.

"See that girl over there in the wheelchair?" she murmured. "Bring her over here. But wait a while, so she doesn't think I sent you."

I waited, and then, as if it was my own idea, I walked

in the girl's direction. Our eyes met. "Hey," I said.

She looked at me and didn't answer.

"Why aren't you with everyone else?'

"'Cause I don't feel like it," she said. She sounded sad. I got that.

"Let's make something interesting," I tried again.

"What for? Because she told you to bring me?"

Full stop. I was about to deny it, but I realized that she was as smart as I was and maybe even smarter.

"You're right. She told me to bring you."

"So tell her that you tried, but I didn't want to come."

"I can't. I'm afraid of her," I confided.

It was her turn to be surprised. "Afraid? Of Ranana? That's a new one."

"She's tough," I said.

"You must mean someone else," she said. "Ranana is the best."

"What difference does it make?" I said. "Tough or the best, just do me a favor and come with me, so I don't get into trouble."

She looked at me with a gleam in her eye. "Sure thing," she said. "I'll come. But you have to tell me what Ranana's like when she's tough."

"You're on," I said. "And you have to tell me about her being the best. Deal?"

"Deal," she said. She sat up straighter and let me help her get over to the balloons.

"What's your name?" I asked her.

"Lele," she said.

"How old are you?" I asked.

"I'm eleven and a half," she said.

"I'm exactly the same age."

"Goody for you," she said, expressionless. I recognized the cynicism.

I wheeled her over to Ranana, who made Lele a special crown of balloons interwoven with real flowers and then sent us on our way.

Lele asked me to bring her to her room, and I did.

I sat down near her, and she told me that she'd been sick for two years and had gone through a lot. She asked if I was Ranana's daughter and I said absolutely not, and then I told her that Ranana was the party planner for my bas mitzvah.

"Oh," Lele said. "I didn't know she did bas mitzvahs. She's known for doing major events. So you're a spoiled rich kid, huh?"

Usually, people who use the expression "spoiled rich kid" don't mean it as a compliment. It's mostly what kids from poor homes call girls who come from wealthy homes.

"I guess you could say that," I admitted. I squirmed a little.

"It's okay. You're nice enough for a rich kid."

You know what? I liked her. She didn't judge me. She was smart and honest.

Suddenly, Ranana was there. "Where did you run off to?" she said to me. "I'm in a rush now."

I said goodbye to Lele, and then I heard myself ask her, "Until when will you be staying here?"

"Until I get better," Lele said. "Which means, there's no expected time."

"Can I come visit you?" I asked.

"Sure." She wasn't enthusiastic but she didn't say no.

* * *

We left.

"What is this place?" I asked Ranana.

"This is the real world," she said. "Not a world of hairstyles and clothes and bickering, but a world of life and mitzvos. Sometimes it's worth visiting this world to put things in perspective."

We returned to her office. She started to present me with ideas. Don't ask. Huge screens, music, food, dances, and of course, the climax: an audio-visual presentation featuring yours truly. But I wasn't really with her. I was far, far away, back in the hospital room with Lele.

"You're not with me," Ranana said.

"You're right," I admitted. "Tell me something. When will you go back there again?"

"In another six days," she said.

"Can I come with you?"

"No problem."

*   *   *

I went with Ranana again, and this time I spent the whole time with Lele. I discovered a very sweet, smart girl who was also fairly cynical. We talked about everything. About her friends and mine, our neighborhoods, our families, and also about her battle with illness.

I really connected with her.

Ranana interrupted us this time too and said, only partially joking, that she couldn't rely on me because I'd disappeared again. The three of us laughed and then Lele said to me, "You can come without her. You're not a baby."

I glanced at Ranana, who shrugged. "Okay," I said.

"Just tell me which buses come here."

When I told my parents, my mother was worried.

"How will you take the bus by yourself? And what will a little girl like you do in the hospital?'

"Mom," I said, "trust me. You might be surprised to hear it, but there are ten-year-old kids who travel by bus. I didn't know that until today, but now that I found out..."

My mother smiled. I saw that despite being slightly worried, she was also pleased.

From then on, I went to visit Lele and also the other kids in her unit.

I told her everything: about my life and my quarrels and my worries, which suddenly all seemed so petty. I told her about the hard road I'd traveled for the bas mitzvah, which, by the way, we still hadn't begun to plan, and about the scary meeting with Ranana.

That really grabbed her attention.

"Did she really say to you, 'Leave this office and don't ever come back'? It's so not like her," Lele said.

"You'll be surprised to hear it, but that's what made me like her," I said.

"You liked her because she talked to you that way?" Lele said. "Excuse me, but you need to see a doctor or something."

We laughed so hard we had to hold our stomachs.

"I don't know," I said. "Maybe it's not so much liking her as trusting her. I felt that I could trust her."

"That makes more sense," Lele said. "You're probably

this spoiled little rich kid, a real JAP, whose parents can't control her. That's probably why you didn't have any self-confidence."

"What's the connection?" I asked her. "What does lack of self-confidence have to do with being a JAP?"

"The connection is that everything you supposedly had really had nothing to do with you. It's like a girl who's never allowed to walk and then is suddenly stood on her own two feet. She'll fall right over.

"Self-confidence isn't something you inherit. You have to work on it. Instead, what did you see? Parents who couldn't stand up to you. So inside you were sort of saying, 'If my own parents, who are my security, are so weak toward me, then I must be a million times weaker.' Do you think self-confidence can come from that?"

"Wow, Lele," I said. "You are so smart. You're like a little psychologist."

Lele ignored me and continued.

"Suddenly you met someone who put you in your place. You encountered the real world. You were a girl full of doubts and hesitations, and she just blew them away. Maybe for the very first time in your life you met an adult who wasn't afraid of you. She led you instead of letting you lead her."

"One hundred percent," I said. "That's exactly how I felt. I feel secure near her."

"Take a good look at yourself," Lele said. "The whole pose you've kept throughout your life was only an act, like a balloon that looks big, but the minute a small pin pricks it, it bursts."

We talked and talked. In time, we became soul sisters. I'd never had a friend before like Lele, a soul mate who knew my life and all its secrets.

Two months went by. My bas mitzvah was getting closer.

My parents started to panic. "What's going to be, Rachelli? You haven't found the time to meet with Ranana, and at the last minute, you'll come complaining to us about your bas mitzvah."

"Don't worry," I said. "I won't come complaining. But I will meet with her because we need to finalize plans."

We met on a Monday exactly two months before my bas mitzvah.

Ranana showed me all the professional audio-visuals she'd ordered and the dances she wanted to teach me and my friends. She also showed me pictures of the clothes we'd need to have made, the hairstyles, the desserts...

"You're not with me, Rachelli," she said suddenly.

I was deep in thought. "Ranana, I don't know how to say this, but none of this appeals to me."

You should have seen her face. If an expression could burn, I would have been burnt to a crisp.

"Are you starting with that?" she said.

"Wait a minute. Just listen to what I want to say. You're not being fair... You took me to the hospital, and there I saw a different world...a world I didn't know existed...and suddenly...and suddenly I realized that I'd been living inside a bubble...and then the bubble burst...and I realized how little I knew and then I met Lele." I started to cry. "I've never met a girl like her before, and she's sick...and I love her so much, and I don't want her to die…"

I saw that Ranana was crying along with me, and I started talking and couldn't stop. I told her about everything that had happened to me since I'd met Lele. I talked and cried for a long time.

In the end, I said to Ranana, "I don't want a hall and a theme and entertainment. I know exactly what I want to do for my bas mitzvah."

Ranana looked at me expectantly.

"You know the hospital lobby? Where they bring all the clowns? That's where I want to have my bas mitzvah. And I want to have it with Lele, who's the same age as I am."

Ranana looked at me in disbelief and then she stood up, walked around the desk, and hugged me. Both of us cried.

She probably had a lot to say, but she didn't need to. Everything was crystal clear.

*   *   *

My bas mitzvah was held in the last place I'd imagined, but in the first place I'd actually wanted.

It wasn't easy. First I needed my parents' approval. Their initial reaction was shock, then they came to terms with it, and finally, when they realized what had happened to me, they were really happy.

From there I had to get my friends and their parents on board.

The double bas mitzvah was a modest affair, without much fanfare, because I'd decided with my parents to donate the huge amount of money they'd planned to spend to the children's ward. We had plenty of food, cakes and drinks and treats, and even a choir of girl singers. The program Lele and I dreamed up was amazing and full of laughter. The party ended with a *kumzitz* that went on for hours.

The singing was so beautiful. We had a keyboard accompany us, too. Even the nurses joined in. Looking back, I realize that this simple bas mitzvah was the most special one ever held for anyone in our school, and not because it cost a lot of money or was full of surprises but because it was simple and natural and full of heart and soul.

Now, almost a year later, I know that this bas mitzvah changed my life. From a spoiled, lazy, and, to put it bluntly, superficial girl, I became a mature girl with depth. I'm not saying that to boast; I hope all that stuff is behind me. I'm saying it to get all of you girls to at least to try it this way.

I received many presents for bas mitzvah, but the biggest present was Lele, the best friend I ever had. I wish you a friend like her and ask that you join me in my prayers for her to have a full recovery. Come with me on my regular visits to her ward. They give so much to the patients...but no less to my soul.

The Gift of Patience

My name is Tehilla.

I'm nine years old, and I live in Yerushalayim.

I'm half.

"Half of what?" you want to know. Half of a set of twins. I have a twin sister named Yehudis.

Yehudis is younger than I am—by five minutes. Don't ask me why I think it's important to mention this. (Even though twins are twins, and everyone looks at us as the same age no matter how often I mention the fact that I'm older.)

Ima told us that before we entered first grade, she consulted with someone in *chinuch*. She wanted to know if we should both be in the same class. He asked her why not, and she answered that she was afraid there would be competition between us.

When we pressed her to explain, she said that she was afraid I would rule over Yehudis because I was the more dominant one and she was quieter. The educational consultant told her that as long as we got along, there was no problem with us being in the same class. In fact, the opposite was true. He thought that each of us would support the other. "Only if you see that one of them is suffering or not developing well would it be a reason to switch one to a different class."

Meanwhile, that hasn't happened.

And the reason it hasn't happened is *because* of the difference between us. Because Yehudis is quiet and I'm noisy, we can each be ourselves, plus get a little help from one another. I "force" Yehudis to express herself when necessary, and Yehudis "forces" me to keep quiet when I talk too much.

The truth? We get along amazingly well. We're very close, we enjoy seeing the other succeed, and we really love each other. I don't know what I would have done without Yehudis, my best, closest friend, and I hope she feels the same way about me.

The story I want to tell is about my last birthday.

Before you ask me why I didn't write "our," it's because my mother always makes us separate birthday celebrations. She explained to us that she feels it's important for us to know that we're not just twins, but that each of us is her own person. She said that when people congratulate two at the same time, it feels like their birthday wishes aren't personal; they're more general. That's why she feels it's important for each of us to celebrate her birthday individually.

* * *

Since I'm the "oldest," my party is always first, and Yehudis has no problem with that. (In case you didn't notice, Yehudis has no problem with almost anything.) Last year, my party was planned for Sunday, so her party would be two days later, on Tuesday.

Naturally, I didn't have anything to do with planning my birthday party. The ones to do that were my mother, Yehudis, and two of my friends, because it would be odd for a girl to plan her own birthday party.

Yehudis's party was planned by my mother, me, and two of Yehudis's friends. (By the way, we have friends who are friends of both of us, but each of us also has some best friends that we don't share.)

Of course, during the same week that Yehudis was planning my birthday party, I was planning hers. Which included, of course, buying a gift.

To me, a gift is something you need to think about a lot. It has to be special, and it should be obvious that a lot of thought went into buying it.

I spent hours discussing with my friends what to buy for Yehudis. All kinds of suggestions were made, but in the end, we decided I would buy her a special piece of jewelry. My mother took me from store to store until I found the perfect gift. I asked the saleswoman to wrap it, and at home, I wrote and attached a note that expressed my deepest feelings for her.

*   *   *

Sunday arrived. They made me a nice party, nothing fancy but tons of fun. Everyone sang and ate cake and ice cream. We played a few games, and everyone gave me presents.

Did I say everyone?

Not exactly. Everyone except for one person.

My sister Yehudis.

Did I say anything at the time? No. Of course not. But I felt really bad. How could it be that she of all people had forgotten?

Yehudis came over to me after the party and said, "I'm sooo sorry. I've just been so busy planning the party that I kept pushing off buying you a present. I

didn't end up getting to it. I'm sure you'll forgive me."

You can hope, I said to myself. *You should be ashamed of yourself! I ran around endlessly, spent hours—no, days!—searching for that perfect present for you, and you didn't even think of me!*

The more I thought about it, the madder I got. By the end of the day, I felt a kind of hatred toward her. Yes. Toward my twin sister.

"I didn't get to it." The more I thought about what she'd said, the more annoyed and mad I felt. What was I, some kind of stranger who just got erased from her memory? Hello! I'm your twin sister! Don't you think I deserve to be remembered?

Monday came, the day before her birthday, and by the afternoon I had made up my mind.

That day there was a birthday party for my best friend, Michal. I said to myself, *If she didn't get to it, then I won't get to it. I'll take the jewelry I bought for her and give it to my friend, who actually brought me a very nice gift.* Okay, it was a stationery set and not a piece of jewelry, because jewelry is something you buy for a sister. But now she's going to be the one to gain. I'll give her the present that I bought for Yehudis. Yehudis proved she's not really a devoted sister; she even forgot to buy me a gift—or, to be more accurate—she "didn't get to it." She couldn't spare me half an hour? Too bad. Then I won't "get to" buy something for her either.

Of course, I slipped up with the mitzvah of not holding a grudge and not taking revenge, but I didn't think about that at all. I just got angrier and made myself miserable over it.

That evening, Michal had her birthday party.

Yehudis was there too. I wrote a different note and gave Michal the gift that was originally intended for Yehudis. I told Michal to open it only after the party was over because I was afraid that she'd exclaim without thinking something like, "Hey, you bought this for your sister." As far as I was concerned, I didn't buy anything for Yehudis, and it was Michal's gift.

*   *   *

Then came Tuesday.

I set up the party for Yehudis together with friends. My lack of enthusiasm was so obvious that they asked me, "What happened to you, Tehilla?"

All I said was, "I don't feel good," which wasn't a lie. I really did feel bad. I felt terrible about what my sister did to me, or, to be more exact, what she *didn't* do *for* me.

The party began with all the girls gathering in our

house to wait for Yehudis, dimming the lights, and shouting "Surprise!" when Yehudis walked in (as if Yehudis didn't know she'd be having a party, the same way I "hadn't known" I was going to have a party two days earlier).

Mazal tov, songs, a program, cake, crafts, group activities, and at the end—one guess—presents!

Everyone gave a present besides me. I saw that Yehudis was waiting for my present, and I hoped she'd realize exactly why she wasn't getting one. I was really waiting for the moment she'd ask me about it, and then I'd answer, "I didn't get to it."

The gift-giving ended. Yehudis had opened each present, oohed and aahed over it, and said thank you to each giver. Some girls looked at me strangely, but I ignored them and wondered, "Why didn't you look at Yehudis that way two days ago? Why are you only remembering now?"

Then it was Yehudis's turn to give a *brachah* and make a speech.

Of course, she thanked everyone for the party, the singing, the activities, and the presents, and then she fell silent. It was obvious that she wanted to say something special, and we all waited.

"Last but far from least, I want to thank my beloved

sister Tehilla, who planned and coordinated this whole amazing party."

Then she started singing my praises, saying what a great sister I am, how interesting and funny I am, how I make her and other people happy, and how I help her with school work and socially.

I blushed. Not only because a lot of people blush when they're praised, but because my quiet sister Yehudis, who hardly ever opened her mouth, was the one saying all these things.

And also…because I knew the kind of thoughts and feelings I'd been having toward her the past two days and how hard my heart was toward her while hers was full of love for me. I started to feel sorry that I'd given her present to a friend. Why did I have to be so petty?

And then came the part that I'll never forget, a moment that taught me so much.

Yehudis said, "I thought about what kind of present could express what I feel. For the past few months, I've been racking my brain and asking other people what present I could give that would show how I feel. Finally, someone suggested that I buy you the special shoes that you like, the ones that can only be bought abroad.

"Dorit's mother made the order, which was supposed to arrive here a couple of weeks ago. For some reason, the shipment was delayed.

"Your birthday party took place two days ago, and the present still hadn't come. I told myself that I just had to give you the present at least by the time of my birthday party.

"You won't believe it, but three hours ago the delivery service delivered the package—your present. I quickly wrapped it up, and here it is."

Yehudis went to over to where she'd hidden the present (behind a cabinet) and took out a beautifully wrapped package.

"This present came from far away to express the love I feel for you," she said, hugging me tight.

I cried...I cried because I was excited, but also because I was upset and ashamed.

How stupid could I have been? Why couldn't I have waited? What had been my big rush to condemn my beloved sister? I'd been so quick to get mad at her and blame her. If I'd had a drop of patience, I wouldn't have gotten angry so fast, and if I hadn't gotten angry, I would have thought calmly and tried to understand what was going on. Maybe I would have even told my sister how I felt and heard from her some comforting words like,

"Don't worry." That would have been enough for me.

But I was too impatient. Too impulsive. And so I had gotten angry and hated her. And worst of all, I had given the present I'd bought for her to someone else. Now there was no way for me to fix what I'd ruined.

* * *

And then, at that very moment, I heard a familiar voice.

It was my friend Michal.

"What did you think, Yehudis?" she said to my sister. "That Tehilla didn't remember you? Very funny. She thought about you a lot. She asked everyone what to get you and then she bought you a very special and expensive gift. Here it is."

Michal pulled out a gift-wrapped box from behind her. Yehudis opened it, and inside was . . .

The jewelry that I'd given Michal the day before.

I was shocked.

Yehudis took the jewelry out of the box and said, "Wow!" Then she hugged me again, and my tears turned into tears of joy.

Later, I approached Michal quietly and asked her, "What was that all about?"

"When I opened the present," Michal said to me, "I

saw right away who it was really for. I also knew why you'd decided to give it to someone else.

"Like everyone else, I knew about the present that was supposed to arrive from abroad. The minute I saw you giving me the present you'd bought for Yehudis, I realized that you'd given me a present out of anger— anger that wasn't justified at all, anger toward your kind, devoted sister who'd been trying for months to find you the perfect present.

"I thought about it and realized that you did it because of one little shortcoming you have. Tehilla, you're the greatest girl and close to a perfect friend, but you've got one little flaw called 'lack of patience.' You're impulsive, and that leads you to make the wrong decisions. I'm your friend. I decided to save you from yourself. I went and bought new gift wrap and waited.

"Sure enough, the minute you got the gift from Yehudis and felt that awful regret, I entered the picture and gave the present, as if we'd planned it that way to begin with. Don't worry. Only you and I know the truth."

I felt a lot of things that I couldn't put into words. I didn't know what to say, so in the end I said, "Michal, I want you to know that you're the truest friend there could ever be. I'm so grateful to you for what you did, and I owe you—"

Michal stopped me. "You owe me only one thing. Tell me that you'll try to be more patient, that you won't make decisions on the spot, that you won't get angry so fast and jump to conclusions. If you do that, you'll be the best friend in the world."

I gave her my word. And ever since, I've tried really hard to keep that promise.

I gave Michal a different gift, but what she and my sister Yehudis taught me, each in her own way, is the biggest gift I could have ever gotten.

The gift of patience.

The Real Winner

My name is Tuvia.

I'm twelve years old, and I'm in seventh grade.

The story I want to tell you took place during last year's summer vacation, and I think every kid in Eretz Yisrael and even the whole world should hear about it.

It starts like this: Just before summer vacation, our school announced a contest called "Honoring Parents."

Each student received a chart divided into dates and tasks. The dates were the days of summer vacation, and the tasks were things like "cleaned room," "helped around the house," and "obeyed parents." There was another box labeled "comments" in which parents could write whatever they wanted.

A parent had to fill in the page every day and sign

it. Any student who submitted a completed chart at the end of vacation would receive a prize. In addition, there would be a valuable prize for "Best in Class" and one grand prize for "Best in School."

Whoever won "Best in School" was actually winning three prizes: a regular prize for filling in all the days, a prize for being the best in class, and the one-and-only grand prize—an expensive bicycle.

You can imagine how excited we were. Everyone wanted to win the "Best in School" prize or at least the "Best in Class" prize. And if not, it wouldn't hurt to win the prize of honoring our parents.

* * *

Vacation began.

Naturally, during the first few days, I cleaned up my room without being told and even asked my mother what else I could do to help. By the end of the week, I'd earned some nice words of praise on the chart, along with my mother's signature.

After that, things started to slide a little. My mother had to nag me to clean up my room. I'd argue a little. But until she said, "I'm not going to be able to fill in the chart," I didn't move.

By the second week, I started wriggling out of

chores with all kinds of excuses like, "I'm tired." "Why doesn't Eli do it?" (Eli's my brother.) "I did it yesterday." You get the idea.

My mother tried pointing to the chart, but it didn't work.

Two days later, I suddenly remembered the chart.

"What do you want me to do?" my mother said. "Do you want me to write that you cleaned your room when you didn't?"

"Please, Ima," I begged. "If you don't fill it in, the chart will be ruined."

After extensive negotiations, we reached an agreement: I would clean the little kids' room, and that would count as if I'd cleaned my own room for the missing days. My mother said she wasn't entirely comfortable with the idea, but she felt sorry for me, so she signed.

That's pretty much how things went, with me skipping chores or avoiding doing what my mother asked.

* * *

One day, a few of my friends decided to go to the pool.

There were four of us, and then I remembered that my friend Yossi had special goggles. It occurred to me that

I should invite him too so that I'd get to use his goggles.

I called his house. Yossi answered.

"Want to come to the pool?" I asked.

"Uh, no. I can't," he said.

"Why not?"

"Uh, I need to help out at home," Yossi said.

"You're taking the contest seriously, huh?"

"I guess you could say that."

"Come on," I told him. "Don't tell me you're taking this contest to the point where you don't even want to go to the pool!"

"Listen, Tuvia, I can't talk right now. But I can't come."

His voice sounded a little strange. He spoke quickly and quietly, as if someone was hovering over him, listening.

"Okay, then. No problem," I said. "If you don't feel like it, that's your business."

Before I got off the phone, I heard him say, "Tuvia."

"Yes?"

"You can stop by for the goggles if you want."

I squirmed. He knew exactly why I had called him.

"Are you sure?" I asked.

"Sure. It's not a problem. I don't think I'll be using them this summer."

I went to his house and knocked on the door. He opened it, but only a crack. I couldn't see anything besides his face. Obviously, he really didn't want me to come in or even see or hear what was going on in the house.

He handed me the goggles.

"Thanks," I said. "But Yossi, are you positive that you don't want to come?"

"Yup. It's fine, Tuvia. But if you don't mind, I'm a little busy right now, okay?"

He closed the door.

I stood there with my mouth open, then shrugged and ran to go swimming with my friends.

*   *   *

We spent a lot of time having fun at the pool. On the way home, I stopped by Yossi's house to return the goggles.

I knocked on the door. It took a long time, but finally, someone opened it.

It was Yossi, wearing an apron.

"Sorry," he said. "I'm in the middle of cooking."

"You're cooking?" I've never cooked anything in my life. It's just something I don't know how to do. I mean, not even an egg. "What's going on?"

He looked uncomfortable. "Nothing much. I just sort of like to cook. It's kind of a secret, uh, hobby."

I handed him the goggles and went home.

* * *

I sat down on the living room couch and thought.

My mother immediately noticed me sitting there like that. "What happened, Tuvia?" she asked. "Is everything okay?"

"Yes," I said.

"How was the pool?"

"Amazing," I said. "It was really fun, and Yossi's goggles made it even better."

"So why are you sitting there all quiet and thoughtful? It's not like you."

"I'll tell you, Ima. Something strange is going on with Yossi."

"Did something happen to him at the pool?"

"No. He didn't even come to the pool." Then I told my mother what I'd seen.

She sat down but didn't say anything.

"What's going on?" I asked. "Do you know anything?"

"Yes," she said. "Now I'm putting two and two together."

I begged my mother to tell me. She hesitated but in the end decided it was appropriate to tell me.

"You probably know that Yossi's mother had a baby recently. Sometimes a new mother has a very rough time, to the extent that she can't function. That's what happened to Yossi's mother. His father is very busy working to support the family. I guess as the eldest child, your friend is taking responsibility for some of the household chores."

"I don't understand. Do you mean to say that his mother isn't even cooking?"

"It can happen," my mother said. "It's possible that a mother in such a situation doesn't do the laundry or cook or take care of the children."

We both sat there in silence.

I thought about it. I pictured what my mother had told me, and I felt bad.

Could it be that Yossi has to dress his little brothers in the morning? That he's the one who makes them breakfast? That he takes care of the laundry? No, it can't be! His father must do it. But what about supper? And who cleans the house? Yossi?

Tears filled my eyes. I thought about Yossi and what he was going through, and I really wanted to cry.

My mother came closer and hugged me.

"What are we going to do, Ima?" I was crying now. "We have to help him!"

"I know that people are helping them," my mother said. "In our community, we step in to support a family in such a situation. But I agree with you that we need to think about how to get them some regular household help as well."

*   *   *

A day passed, and I asked my mother what was happening. She told me that Yossi's mother refused to allow cleaning help in her home and there was no way to convince her.

I started asking questions. I couldn't understand how such a thing was possible.

Finally, my mother said, "Some things you'll only understand when you're an adult. Sometimes people find themselves in a tough spot and don't know how to get out of it. We need to daven that she gets better, and in the meantime, do all we can to help Yossi."

It turns out that my mother had arranged for a few other mothers to help. They sent in meals that they took turns cooking and they did the laundry, but they hadn't been able to enter the house, so all the house-keeping work fell on Yossi.

I managed to convince Yossi to come with us to all kinds of places, but as far as helping in the house, the answer was no. He absolutely refused to let us in.

*　*　*

Then summer vacation ended, and on the first day of school, we all handed in our "Honoring Parents" charts. According to the rules of the campaign, the school would announce the results within a week. After examining the pages, they'd name the winners.

I looked at my friends' charts. I noticed that in every chart, the first few days' squares were filled with all sorts of major help to their parents, but after that, it got less and less. I also had a drop after the first week, but then an increase.

Only I knew why.

Ever since I'd heard Yossi's story, I'd been too ashamed to say no to my mother. I found myself helping all the time, and being very careful not to upset my parents.

As I was sitting in class and thinking about all this, I suddenly felt worried. I went over to Yossi and said to him, "Your chart must be crowded with entries. The way you're helping your parents is amazing."

He didn't answer right away. Then he said, "I

didn't hand it in yet. My father needs to fill it in, but he's very busy now, and he didn't have time."

After school, I ran home and told my mother, "Ima, I found out that Yossi didn't bring in his chart. I guess his mother can't fill it out. We can't let that happen! It's not fair. No one deserves to win more than Yossi!"

My mother listened to me and then said, "You are so right, Tuvia. Good for you that you noticed. I hope his father will fill out the chart. Or maybe his mother will become stronger and be able to do it. He really deserves it."

*   *   *

A week later, the awards ceremony took place.

Ten boys in my class who met the conditions of the contest won prizes, including me. (It turns out that a lot of boys had dropped out. At a certain point, they stopped helping and just gave up.)

Then the prizes were given out to the most outstanding boy in each class.

The principal called one boy from each class (we have twenty-something classes). I won as the outstanding student in my class.

I went up and accepted my prize with mixed feelings. On the one hand, I was happy, like any kid who gets a prize. On the other hand, I didn't think it was fair. I knew that Yossi deserved it more than I did. The fact that his parents hadn't filled in the chart just proved what a hero he was, doing everything on his own. It was only thanks to Yossi that I'd gotten a prize at all, and he didn't even get one! To me, that made no sense.

While I was preoccupied with these thoughts, the awards ceremony for "Best in Class" ended. Now we all waited to see who would win the triple grand prize. (Whoever got it had already won two other prizes.)

The principal took the microphone and said, "As is the case every year, this year we received pages filled with descriptions of *kibbud av va'eim*. Usually, the mother is the one who fills out the chart, and sometimes the father adds to it as well. But this year, for the very first time in the history of our school, we received many pages about one boy—a boy who helped his parents more than any other boy since this school was founded."

I sat there, feeling confused. Was it possible that any boy had worked harder than Yossi? And had received *ten pages* of comments? That seemed impossible to me, and I was very curious to know who it was.

"Ten mothers wrote about one boy who is not their son—a boy who helped his parents more than any other boy in this school.

"To these ten pages, they attached a letter of

explanation. They said that their children participated in the contest. They cleaned their rooms and at times helped around the house. But, they wrote, this boy did far more than that. He took upon himself responsibility for many more household chores in order to spare his parents, who were very busy. He cooked, he did laundry, he helped his brothers and sisters—all without being asked. He honored his parents by shouldering as much of their burden as he could.

"This boy not only taught other students how to help around the house, he actually modeled what it means to honor one's father and mother and served as a shining example for all our students of how to honor one's parents. For this reason, we have chosen him for the 'Best in School' award."

Then the principal called Yossi's name.

* * *

Yossi was in shock.

I saw him just before the announcement, looking sad and withdrawn. Now his eyes suddenly lit up. He walked up onto the stage to the sound of applause and accepted the grand prize from the principal and the assistant principal.

He'd won the jackpot.

* * *

That's the story of last year's vacation.

Yossi's mother recovered—my mother had told me at the time that it's usually temporary and that most new mothers recover after a while—and Yossi was released from the heavy burden he'd carried. He went back to being a regular kid who helped his parents, but he no longer ran the house.

He did tell me, though, that he's not willing to give up cooking.

But only as a hobby.

There's another contest this year, but I can tell you right now that I'm going to keep on helping my parents and honoring them whether there's a contest or not. Yossi's story made me understand what it means to honor parents.

I get it now. Doing the mitzvah *is* itself the grand prize. And I'll be on the lookout for ways to win it.

Was That an Invitation?

My name is Yehudit.

I'm twelve and a half, and I'm in the sixth grade.

I want to tell you about my bas mitzvah (actually, mine and my cousin Yael's). Not exactly about it, but about something I understood because of it, something that every kid can relate to.

Yael and I aren't only cousins; we're best friends too. I'm half a year older, but we've never felt the age difference because six months isn't such a big deal and because we've been together since we were born (or, to be more accurate, since she was born). At six months old, I didn't really notice the age difference, and that's continued until today.

We meet almost every Shabbos at our grandmother's house (our fathers are brothers), or we go to each other's houses, where we play and talk. We don't go to the same school, but that doesn't detract from our friendship.

* * *

Half a year ago, I had a bas mitzvah party.

At the school's request, the bas mitzvah party was held in our home. We invited family and neighbors and my two good friends from school.

Naturally, I invited Yael. She came and even brought me a present.

As small and family-oriented as my bas mitzvah was, it was a lot of fun. My cousins planned the program and activities. We danced, the food was amazing, and I was super happy with the party.

I thanked Yael profusely for coming and for the present she'd given me, but I didn't get the response I expected. She listened, said "great," and then changed the subject. I thought it was a little strange, but this was the first time something like this had happened, so I didn't pay it too much attention.

In the coming months, though, every time I talked about my bas mitzvah party, Yael would change the subject. What was going on?

One day I asked her about it. "Yael, why don't you want to talk about my bas mitzvah party?"

She shrugged and said, "What's there to talk about? It was nice. Move on."

I was almost insulted, but I knew Yael so well. She wasn't the type to say hurtful things. At all. She was always kind and considerate.

I decided to move on and not make a big deal out of it. My father always tells us, "Before you decide to feel insulted, think about whether it will be worth it." When he first said that, I didn't understand what he meant. If I felt hurt, what did that have to do with it being worth it for me or not? But as I got older, I realized that most of the time when we feel hurt, we don't gain anything by it; we lose. We lose friends, we lose our good mood, and we lose out on fun. The only thing we "gain" from feeling hurt is fights and heartache.

* * *

A month before she turned twelve, I asked Yael, "What are you planning for your bas mitzvah?"

She shrugged and said, "I have no idea. My mother's planning it."

"You're not planning it with her?" I asked.

"Not really," she said. "My mother's planning it."

She'd said that already. And if she thought I'd be put off by that answer, she was right. Who wants to ask a question when you already know that the answer will be, "My mother's planning it"?

Two weeks before the date, I took the risk of asking her again. "So, what are the plans?"

"My mother is taking care of everything. I don't know exactly when it will be."

What kind of an answer was that? I'm sure you'll agree with me that it seemed very evasive.

The more I thought about it, the more I realized that it didn't just "seem" evasive; it was evasive.

*　*　*

Two weeks passed. One day, Yael's mother called my mother and said, "Tomorrow is Yael's bas mitzvah. Yehudit can come, but she doesn't have to."

"It's tomorrow?"

"Yes," my aunt said. "We'd be happy to see her, but she doesn't have to come."

My mother ended the call and told me that I was invited to Yael's bas mitzvah but that I didn't have to go.

"What's that supposed to mean?" I asked her.

"I have no idea," my mother said. "That's what she said: 'She doesn't have to come.' Maybe she thinks it's a bother for you to come."

I gave my mother a look we both understood: A

bother? To go to a bas mitzvah party? Huh?

The next day, the day of the bas mitzvah, I went with my mother to buy a present. We got something nice and fairly expensive, and then I said to my mother, "But why should I go if Yael didn't even invite me and her mother said, 'She doesn't have to come'?"

"I thought about that, and I discussed it with Abba," my mother said. "In our family, we don't make calculations. If you're invited, you go."

Yes, I know that the expression "You don't make calculations" is a close cousin of "Don't get insulted because it doesn't pay," but with all due respect to the similarity of those two sayings, I needed to attend the bas mitzvah party of a cousin who didn't invite me despite a strange invitation from her mother who didn't really invite me.

*   *   *

I couldn't decide whether to go or not, but when four o'clock came around, I decided to go, both because "you don't make calculations," and also because I just wanted to be at my cousin Yael's bas mitzvah, even if I didn't have to.

I went there, and for the first time in my life I felt that I was going to Yael's house feeling nervous and worried instead of excited.

I walked up the two flights of stairs and knocked on the door. Yael's mother opened it.

"Oh!" she exclaimed. "How embarrassing. The bas mitzvah party was pushed back two hours, so it will start at six, not four. I forgot to tell your mother. I'm so sorry."

I didn't say anything. I felt a lump in my throat.

"Is Yael here?" I asked.

"No," her mother said. "She went shopping with two cousins to get a few last-minute items. Ruti and Racheli. You probably don't know them. They're from our side of the family."

Actually, I did know them from all the *simchos* I'd gone to on Abba's side of the family. My father is Yael's uncle, and Ruti and Racheli are Yael's cousins "from the other side." I considered saying that, but there was no point.

Besides, I was afraid that if I talked, I'd start to cry.

I gave her the gift, turned around, and began walking down the stairs.

"You can come at six," I heard her say, "but you don't need to go to the trouble of coming all this way again."

I had already turned the corner, so she couldn't see the tears that sprang to my eyes, and since she'd closed the door, she couldn't hear me cry.

I was crying hard because I felt so hurt. (I didn't stop to think about whether or not it paid for me to feel hurt. I was just hurt, that's all.) I huddled in the corner and wept, and then when I ran out of tears, I went home and told my mother about it and cried again.

The two hours passed, and of course I did not go to bas mitzvah. This time I did make calculations, and my mother didn't stop me. She totally understood.

* * *

When my father came home, I told him everything. He listened and looked very surprised.

He said, "What you're telling me sounds very strange because we know Doda Chedva (Yael's mother), and she's not like that."

"True," my mother said. "And because she's not like that, it's very strange."

"Maybe she really is like that!" I said. I burst out crying for the third time.

My parents hugged me and consoled me and promised that they would find out what had happened.

I protested vehemently. "I don't want you to talk about it! I'll look like someone who people are forced to invite to a bas mitzvah party that she wasn't invited to."

"But you were invited to it," my father said.

"But you don't have to come," my mother and I said in unison. We burst out laughing, which sort of cleared the air.

I went to sleep. My father and mother kept talking in the living room. I didn't hear what they said, but I knew they were talking about it, and that made me feel good. I trust my parents. They're very involved in our lives and make sure to take care of anything that bothers us. I knew they wouldn't leave things as they were.

Though I'd adamantly protested that I didn't want them to talk about it with Yael's parents, deep inside I did want them to. You're probably the same: we say one thing (because we're afraid or ashamed), but inside we want something else, that someone else should do the work for us even without our permission. My parents are smart enough to understand this, and I can count on them. When I really don't want them to do anything, I know how to tell them that.

* * *

In the end, my parents didn't need to do a thing. The following afternoon, Yael's mother called.

When I picked up the phone, she asked for my mother and started apologizing to her.

"I'm so sorry I didn't tell you about the change of

time. I was so busy. I notified everyone, but forgot you. Thank you so much for the present. It's the most expensive one she got."

My mother didn't say anything.

"Hello?" Doda Chedva said. "Are you there?"

"I'm listening," my mother said tersely.

"Is everything okay?"

"Not exactly," my mother said. "The problem is not the delay. The problem is that Yehudit didn't participate in Yael's bas mitzvah."

"But we invited her," Doda Chedva said. "I'm really sorry we forgot to tell her about the time change. I'm sure you can understand how busy I was. I told one of the cousins about the delay and asked her to pass on the message."

"My dear Chedva, I'm not talking about that," my mother said. "If I would invite you verbally to a simchah and tell you five times 'you don't need to come,' would you come?"

Chedva fell silent.

My mother continued. "And if you would still come, ignoring all the not-so-subtle hints, only to discover that the event was pushed off two hours, and I would apologize and say to you, 'I feel very uncomfortable, but the party is delayed, and I forgot to tell you that it won't take place for another two hours, but you really, really don't need to come'—would you come?"

Chedva was silent for a long time, and then finally she said, "You're right. I wouldn't come. But what I said wasn't because I didn't want her to come but because we were afraid, Yael and I, that Yehudit wouldn't feel comfortable at the bas mitzvah. There were only cousins from our side, because Yael doesn't have much of a connection with her cousins from your side of the family. On our husbands' side, there aren't that many girls this age, and they hardly know the ones from your side, so Yael was sure that Yehudit would feel awkward and left out, and I thought so too. That's why it was important for me to emphasize it. I'm so sorry. It really doesn't sound good."

Chedva continued to explain, and my mother said, "Fine. I'll tell that to Yehudit; she's very hurt." Then I heard her add, "And I'll try to understand it myself."

Doda Chedva apologized again, and the call ended.

*   *   *

We looked at each other. My mother asked me, "Well, what do you think?"

"I don't know," I said. "What do you think, Ima?"

"It sounds like an excuse," she said, "but evidently it's the truth. We've known Doda Chedva for many years. She's a wonderful person. She's not someone who makes calculations. Maybe she made a mistake, but she did it out of caring for you. Maybe the thought was wrong, but her intentions were good. It didn't come from a bad place."

This was so like my mother. She and my father have good hearts and always see the positive side of things.

A few hours later, we heard someone knocking on the door.

I opened the door and standing there before me was…Yael.

"May I come in?" she asked.

"Please," I said.

In our house, we welcome guests nicely no matter what the circumstances.

We went to my room and sat down. The silence dragged on until Yael broke it.

"Look, Yehudit, I know that you feel hurt by my mother, but it's important for me that you know the truth. It's not really my mother."

"Aha," I said. "Then I guess there's someone with exactly the same voice as your mother, and you won't believe how she looks exactly like your mother, and, big coincidence, she just happened to be in your house yesterday."

Yael laughed, but after one look at me, she stopped.

"That's not what I meant," she said. "It was my mother who called to invite you. And it was my mother who said you don't have to come. She's the one you gave the present to when she opened the door, and she's the one who told you that the party was pushed off by two hours and said, again, that you weren't obligated to come."

Do you find this confusing? I did too.

"What I wanted to say," Yael said, "is that none of this was coming from her. I'm the one who asked her to make it crystal clear to you that you didn't need to come."

"Oh, that makes me feel so much better," I said sarcastically. "And here I was sure that you wanted to see me, and it was just your mother. Now I see that it's you, the cousin I'm closest to, the one who came to my bas mitzvah."

"That's exactly what I wanted to talk to you about," Yael said. "Let's talk about your bas mitzvah. I came, all excited and happy. I brought a nice present with a note that was even nicer. I was so looking forward to your bas mitzvah.

"But when I arrived, I didn't see anyone I knew. You'd invited the cousins from your mother's side, because on our father's side there aren't any girls our age except us. You didn't invite any girls from our side—that is, my mother's side—and now I understand why. Because you don't know them.

"It was like I was invisible. I sat down, and no one paid me any attention. Of course not. They didn't know me. One girl asked who I was and what I was doing there. I started to explain that I was your cousin on your father's side, but she went to talk to someone else, so I was sitting there alone again.

"The only person I knew was you, but you were busy with your friends, and I didn't blame you for it. Okay, maybe a little. I expected you to notice me, to tell everyone that I was your cousin—and not only your cousin, but a close friend. You didn't do it, and I totally understood. You were busy with your party; how could you find time for a cousin from the other side?"

"When I left your bas mitzvah party, I cried. I came home with red eyes, and I was mad at you.

"It was my mother who calmed me down and explained that it wasn't your fault; you couldn't be expected to notice such things on such a special day. She told me it was a shame we hadn't known who would be coming, because if we had, we could have given some elegant excuse for not attending just to preserve the peace. You would have been happy, and I wouldn't have left feeling miserable.

"As we prepared for my bas mitzvah, we knew that I wasn't going to invite girls I didn't know, like cousins on a second or third side. That's when I mentioned your name and asked my mother what to do.

"My mother thought about it a long time until finally she said, 'I'm sure that Yehudit invited you only to be polite. She didn't think it would make you uncomfortable, and she couldn't have anticipated what happened. Now she knows, and she's probably hesitant to come to your bas mitzvah, but she'll come just to be polite and be bored through it. I think the only way to prevent her from experiencing the suffering you went through is to invite her, yet give her a way out, so she knows she doesn't have to come. We'll make it clear to her that she doesn't have to come, and she'll surely realize why we're saying it.'

"And that's exactly what my mother did. She didn't consider one thing, though: that you wouldn't understand. And when I thought about why you didn't understand, I came to a conclusion that was tough to face. I realized that you had no idea how much I'd suffered, how lonely I'd felt at your bas mitzvah. I'd assumed that you would have realized it on your own. At that moment, though, it struck me that you hadn't thought about me at all."

Tears welled up in her eyes.

*   *   *

Wow. I was shocked! The whole picture suddenly changed.

She was right. I'd been so absorbed in my bas mitzvah, I hadn't given a thought to Yael and how she was feeling. Now I was finding out that she had suffered through it, and because she didn't want me to go through the same suffering, she'd found a clever way to help me avoid it.

Why hadn't I ever thought of it? I'd been too busy thinking about myself, that's why.

Suddenly, the whole picture shifted.

"I'm sorry, Yael," I heard myself say. "I don't understand how I acted like that at my bas mitzvah, and until this minute, I never imagined things from your point of view. Do you forgive me?"

Yael cried, but it was a cry of relief. "I'm glad you understand. Everything I was trying to do was for your benefit, yet look what happened."

"Don't worry about it," I said. "Nothing bad came out of it. Let me call my mother."

I asked my mother to come into the room. She looked nervous. She realized that something had happened.

"You and Abba always say we need to hear the other side of the story. Now I want to tell you Yael's side."

I told her in my own words what had happened to Yael at my bas mitzvah, and how Yael and her mother thought of a way to keep me from similar suffering.

My mother was moved to tears. She hugged and kissed Yael and asked her forgiveness and immediately said, "I want to call your mother to apologize."

Yael and I stayed in my room. We both realized that this was a moment we'd always remember, a moment when we understood how different people's thoughts are (as different as their faces), and how important it is to check things out, to talk about everything, and never to draw conclusions before we knew the whole story.

I hope that our story and its important message will reach as many children as possible.

Judge everyone favorably! And if you can't do it by yourself, listen to the other side of the story. Most of the time, the explanation will satisfy us and help us live our lives without quarreling or controversy, without insults, and without…making calculations.

The Contact Lens

My name is Chezky.

I'm twelve years old, and I live in Ramat Beit Shemesh.

Whenever my parents came back from a PTA meeting, they brought back a few comments that will sound familiar to some of you: *"He's not reaching his full potential."*

"He has a lot of talent."

"If he believed in himself, he could be tops."

On the surface, these sound like very positive statements. But every kid understands what's behind them.

Behind the sentence "He's not working up to his potential" stands another sentence: "He's not working at class level." Behind "He has a lot of talent" stands "Too bad he doesn't use it." And behind the last sentence, "If he believed in himself, he could be tops," there's another sentence that says, "He has low self-esteem, which is why he ranks twenty-seventh in a class of twenty-eight."

It's not that I had complaints when they said these things to me; I deserved it. On the contrary, I should have thanked the teachers for not saying the truth more bluntly and for trying to see the positive side.

The bottom line? I was considered a lazy kid. I can come up with many reasons to explain it, but none of them are a real excuse. The truth is, other kids put in the effort but I didn't. What more is there to say?

During last summer, something happened that changed everything.

Our school's summer camp took us on an overnight trip to a huge waterpark. We reached the park and raced to see who would be first on the waterslides and tubes.

Fifteen minutes later, our *rebbi* announced that he'd lost his contact lens in the pool.

We all felt bad for him. There's no way to find a contact lens in a pool. Maybe if you work hard at it you can find a pair of glasses, but a contact lens? We sympathized and continued to play, slide, and swim.

After about an hour and a half, they announced a break.

We gathered on the grass, where we were each given a roll and chocolate milk. Then we had an hour's learning session with our *rebbi*, and then we went back to the pools and the slides.

No one had any patience for learning. We all finished our roll and chocolate milk and sat or stood restlessly near the *rebbi*.

He began to tell us something. I don't think any of us paid attention. But it didn't seem to matter to him because there's a difference between school and camp. What mattered to him was that everyone sat quietly without wandering around or interrupting.

Ten minutes later, a friend of mine said to me, "Did you notice that he can hardly see out of his left eye? That's the one that the contact lens fell out of."

I looked again and saw that the *rebbi* was acting strange. He had everyone on his right under control. But if there was any disturbance on his left, he turned his whole head to speak to the kid. Which was strange, because they were right there in front of him.

It took us time to understand that his left eye wasn't really functioning right then and that in order to see on the left, he had to turn his right eye to the left while the left eye looked backward. (Try it, and you'll see what I'm talking about.)

A few kids stayed far to the *rebbi's* left, outside his field of vision. To see them, he had to turn his head around, which gave them plenty of time to stop talking, jumping, running, laughing, or anything else he had asked us not to do.

I know it's wrong to take advantage of someone's weakness, but we didn't think about it. It was so much fun that he couldn't see on the left that we took advantage of it.

He quickly caught on and told us, "What you're doing isn't nice. It's hard enough for me as it is. Try to listen for a few more minutes and then we'll all go back to the pool."

I can't say we paid much attention. Maybe we tried, but not that hard, and not with much success.

When the learning session ended, he let us go to the pool. We raced away and stormed the attractions for another two hours.

All this time, he was sitting on the grass. Some boys went over to him and asked, "Rebbi, why aren't you going in?"

"The trip is already ruined for me, but at least I'd like to keep my other contact lens if possible."

* * *

It turned out to be a permanent lens, not the kind you replace every day. Kids who wear contact lenses probably know what that means. I don't.

I was beginning to feel sorry for my *rebbi*. I said to my friends, "Let's look for the lens in the pool."

Everyone burst out laughing.

"Are you kidding, Chezky?"

"No," I said. "If we all look, maybe we'll find it."

"I'm willing to bet that we won't," said Shmulik, who bets on everything. Sometimes he wins, and sometimes he loses—but he never pays.

"You're not allowed to bet," I told him, "but I'm telling you that there's a chance we may find it."

My friend Michael stood up for me. "What do you care? Let's try."

Our *rebbi*, who heard the conversation, said, "I'm against getting involved, but Chezky, I'd hate to see you and the others waste your time and effort on this. There's no chance of finding a contact lens in a pool."

"Rebbi," I said, "we're bored with just swimming around in the pool. If we swim and dive for a goal, it will be a challenge for us."

"Okay," he said. "Have fun. But remember all the pool rules—and be careful!"

Five boys (to his credit, Shmulik was one of them)

headed for the pool and began searching for the contact lens.

After five minutes, everyone gave up.

"I told you it didn't make sense," said Shmulik, and this time everyone agreed with him, including Michael.

I had no answer, so I didn't say anything. But I was thinking, *The lens has to be somewhere in this pool. If a few kids look for it for a few hours, they'll find it.*

I decided not to say anything. I shrugged my shoulders, pretending to give up like the others. I let them go, and then I put my goggles back on and dove into the pool.

The pool was paved with small four-inch square blue tiles. I decided to go through the pool, tile by tile.

I gave each tile half a second. I went through about fifty tiles before coming up to breathe. Then I dove under again.

I began at the shallow end of the pool. I knew that searching in the deep end would be much harder; just going down to the bottom is hard enough.

I have no idea how long I was at the pool. I do know that the two hours must have finished, because the rest of the kids left to get dressed for the night activity.

I stayed in the pool.

If you ask me, this was a big mistake—both on my

part and on the lifeguard's. No one was supposed to leave a kid in the pool.

But that's what happened. I stayed there and looked and looked until suddenly, I noticed that I was alone.

I noticed something else, too. Those were the last few minutes of our class's turn to be in the pool. Soon, even if I wanted to, I wouldn't be able to look anymore.

I made one last dive at the deep end. And then...

There it was on one of the tiles.

It was resting there like a mini transparent yarmulke. If not for the edge that looked like a circle, I'd never have seen it.

With a trembling hand, I turned it over and stuck it onto the tip of my finger. Then I made a fist, keeping it tightly closed around that finger so the lens couldn't fall out, and rushed to the surface to breathe.

I got out of the pool. I felt...indescribable, like I'd won a race or something. Not against anyone else, but against something. I realized that I had accomplished something that no one believed could be done—with *siyata d'Shmaya* and willpower.

I climbed out of the pool. Everyone had dressed already.

I arrived at the spot where my class was waiting,

saw the *rebbi* look in my direction, and ran quickly to join the group of boys on his left side. I heard him say, "Wait a minute. Who's that over there who isn't dressed yet?"

I slipped away somehow and blended in with the crowd. I dressed quickly and stood with the whole class.

The *rebbi* said to me, "True, I don't see well with my left eye, but with my right eye I saw that you just left the pool. It's very dangerous to be in the pool when there's no lifeguard."

I lowered my eyes.

"Rebbi, he was looking for your lens," Shmulik said.

"That's not worth the risk," he said, and then suddenly stopped.

"We gave up after five minutes," Michael said, "but Chezky didn't."

"Wait a minute," my *rebbi* said. "Do you mean to tell me that for—" he looked at his watch "—two hours you were in the pool, trying to find my contact lens?"

I nodded.

"Listen, I have nothing to say to you. I still protest that you stayed in the pool after everyone left, but allow me to admire you for sticking to a goal. But you need to know that sometimes when things are lost, they're gone forever. Too bad you wasted all that time and effort for nothing."

"Why for nothing?" I asked.

"Because looking for a contact lens in a swimming pool is like trying to find a needle in a haystack. The only result for both is disappointment."

Without a word, I walked up to the *rebbi*, opened the hand that was still closed tightly around the contact lens, and asked, "Is this your contact lens?"

Wow!

Everyone was stunned.

The *rebbi* looked at the contact lens, took it with his finger, and put it into his left eye.

"I don't believe it," he said. "How did you find it?"

I didn't say anything. I myself don't know how I did it.

The *rebbi* gave me a pat on the back. He was so excited that he found it hard to talk. He was in shock, like everyone else.

After a while, he said, "It says in *Tehillim* 119, 'From all my teachers I gained understanding.' In the Gemara in *Ta'anis*, Rabbi Chanina says, 'And from my students more than all.' Everyone here just saw an example of Rabbi Chanina's teaching.

"I must admit that I never thought this contact lens

could be found. But Chezky thought differently, and he decided to do his utmost to find it. And against all odds, he did. Do you know why? Because he had an overwhelming desire to succeed.

"Chezky, you have proven to yourself and to us that 'nothing stands in the way of willpower.' This obligates me and your friends, but most of all it obligates you. If you could find a contact lens in a pool that size, there's nothing in the world you can't achieve."

The story about me finding the contact lens was a sensation that people talked about for a long time.

For me it was huge. It made me believe in myself.

The following year, I accomplished many goals that in the past I'd never even dreamed of, for instance, getting a hundred on every test and coming to school on time every day.

One day in the middle of the year, our last-year's *rebbi* substituted for our regular *rebbi*. He gave us the test our *rebbi* had prepared for us. I finished the test quickly, but before I handed it in, the boy sitting next to me whispered to me that he wanted to copy from me.

I let him—maybe because it wasn't our regular *rebbi*. We switched papers, and I let him look at my answers until the time was almost up.

I stood up, went up to the substitute, and handed him my test paper.

He took it, then leaned close and whispered in my ear, "I saw what you did. You gave your test to the boy sitting next to you. I'll have to do something about it."

I was speechless. The punishment for copying is serious.

But then he said to me, "But I saw it with my left eye, so I didn't see it." He winked at me and signaled that I could leave.

I walked away with a warm feeling in my heart. He wanted to tell me that he felt indebted for my efforts so he'd let it go. It was a terrific ending to my story.

Every once in a while, when I do some soul searching, I realize that my *rebbi's* lost lens and the way I found it against all odds made me see things I never would have seen before—all the strengths I have, and the importance of willpower and persistence.

The Saddest Birthday Boy

My name is Yigal.

I'm twelve years old, and I live in Givat Shmuel.

I'm a friendly kid, and some people think I'm the most popular boy in our class. I'm not telling you that to brag, but it's important for you know that about me before you read the story I'm about to tell you.

I'd like as many kids as possible hear this story, which is why I sent it to Kids Speak at POB 211, Bnei Brak. That way I know it will reach loads of kids everywhere.

Now for the story.

* * *

I'm sure those of you who are in school know what I mean when I talk about fitting in and being accepted by the group.

There are kids who are accepted and kids who are less accepted. And then there are those who aren't accepted at all. You might even say they're rejected by the group.

Why? No one knows the reason. Sometimes the kid is too quiet, but on the other hand, there are those quiet kids who everyone likes. Sometimes there's a kid or a few kids in class who decide to pick on a classmate, bully him, or just plain ignore him.

Until recently, I didn't pay any attention to stuff like that. I would just arrive at school every day, looking forward to whatever interesting things would happen with my friends, and I'd come home bursting with experiences.

It's not that I didn't know there were kids who weren't part of the group; it's just that I didn't pay much attention to it. Maybe because I was busy with my own life—and maybe because I'd never felt what they were feeling.

* * *

A few months ago, during summer vacation, my whole family (my parents and three siblings) went to a hotel in Yerushalayim for a week.

One evening we went to eat in a restaurant.

We walked in, were shown to a table, and were given menus.

Right next to us was a round table decorated with balloons, colorful napkins, and a fancy tablecloth. Near the table stood a man who looked old enough to be my grandfather. He was busy rearranging things on the table to make it look better. Then he tied a helium balloon to each chair. When that was done, he tied a balloon to each bottle on the table and sat down.

I wondered how anyone would be able to pour from those bottles.

A few minutes passed, and then he got up again and tied a second balloon to each chair. The round table looked like a stage surrounded by a wall of balloons.

When the waiter came to take our orders, my father asked him to come back in a few minutes because we were having a hard time making up our minds. Besides, we couldn't help but watch as the elegant round table next to us became more and more decorated with each passing minute.

The man placed clown hats on each plate, tried on one himself, and then sat down. He soon stood up and, still wearing the clown hat, began lining up the plates and silverware until they were symmetrical.

He wore a clown's hat, but it wasn't funny. At all.

And just wait and see—we didn't even know yet how not funny it was.

My father was the first to speak to him. "Tell me something, Reb Yid." ("Reb Yid" is my father's friendly greeting to people he doesn't know.)

"You're probably making a birthday party for a grandchild, aren't you?"

The man looked at my father as if he was glad that someone had finally noticed him. "No, my friend," he said. "It's a birthday celebration, but not for a grandchild."

"Then for one of your children?" my father guessed.

"Not for one of my children, either," he said. "Partly because I have no children and thus no grandchildren, and before you ask about my wife, let me tell you that the party isn't for my wife either, and that's because I never married, so how could I make a birthday party for my wife if I never married?" He laughed.

Now it was getting really sad. We laughed, but not because it was funny. We laughed because he laughed. He must have thought that what he said was funny, and it's only polite to laugh when someone makes a joke. (I admit that I didn't act this politely with my friends. But because I laughed with this elderly man whom I felt bad for, I saw that it's possible to laugh with anyone.)

"It's a party for *me*," the man said. "Today I turned seventy, and though I don't have a wife or children, I do have a few friends. Or at least I thought I did. Now I see that I don't even have a few friends. Why? Because I called each one and invited him to attend the birthday party I was making for myself. Some said, 'I'll try to make it,' and some said they'd come, but I've been here for nearly an hour, and no one's shown up. They're probably too busy to join me to celebrate my seventieth birthday. Or maybe they just forgot about it."

You've got to realize that he said everything exactly the way I wrote it—all while standing next to the fancy table with a clown's hat on his head. I'd never seen a sadder sight. My little sister started to cry, and I felt tears welling up in my eyes.

And then my father said, "You know what? *We'll* celebrate your birthday with you. How does that sound?"

"Really?" The man's expression brightened. "Are you sure...your family would be interested in something like that?"

"Let's ask them," my father said, but before he could ask us, we all said, "Of course we want to make you a birthday party!"

In no time at all, we got up from our table and moved to the fancy table. At the last minute, a family from a nearby table that had been watching joined as well.

The waiters began serving, and then my father said to the man, "In our family, the custom is that on a person's birthday, everyone at the party says something in praise of the birthday celebrant. But we've got a little problem here because we don't know you that well. So perhaps you would be willing to tell us a bit about yourself, and then we can offer some words of praise in honor of your birthday."

At first, the man seemed uncomfortable, but because my father spoke to him as if it was no big deal, he started to talk.

"There's not much to praise me about," the man began. "I was born here in Eretz Yisrael seventy years ago. My parents were simple folk, honest and hardworking, and very quiet. They hardly had any friends.

"Even when I was in kindergarten, I didn't have any friends, but I didn't realize it then. From the moment I went to school I knew that there were thirty kids around me, but they didn't see me as one of them.

"In second grade they started to tease me. If you ask me, there was no reason for them to tease me. I didn't do anything bad to anyone, and I didn't take anything from a single kid. The opposite was true; I was as quiet as the tables or chairs in the classroom.

"But one day a boy called me a name and then everyone else called me that name and then they started to laugh at me and tease me.

"In later years, I got hit too. Out of nowhere a boy would come over and hit me.

"I didn't tell my parents, but the teacher told them that I was being bullied. My parents didn't know what to do, so they transferred me to a different school.

"I thought I was saved, but it turned out that the move didn't help me at all. Instead, things got worse.

"The children quickly caught on that I was a quiet boy with no self-confidence, and they too decided to bully me and hit me. But what hurt even more was when they ignored me.

"What did my parents do? You guessed correctly. They switched me to a different school.

"There, you'll be surprised to hear, something changed.

"Right at the beginning, a boy welcomed me and became my friend.

"I'll never forget how happy I was. I felt like the happiest boy in the world.

"All at once, I had a friend who came to my house and invited me to his. I started to enjoy going to school and felt very good about myself.

"But it didn't last.

"After six months, a boy started bullying me and my friend. The two of us became outcasts. True, it was better than what I was used to, but again I returned to being the poor, rejected boy. I felt bad, too, because I thought that my friend was suffering only because of me.

"One day, my friend left, and I was left alone.

"I went from being a child to being a teenager. My teenage years were even worse than my childhood because now I understood what friends meant and what it meant to be all alone, and it broke my heart.

"Everyone got used to me being the type who didn't open his mouth, the boy on the sidelines, and I got used to it too.

"I turned twenty-five and then thirty. All my classmates got married, but I couldn't find a wife. I got plenty of suggestions, but I was shy and lacking self-confidence, and all the girls suggested to me sensed it right away.

"Meanwhile, my parents aged. When my father died, I was left alone with my mother.

"I started a computer business even before everyone owned calculators. I sold time- and attendance-tracking software to businesses. It was my idea to computerize the field, and soon the biggest businesses and factories were using my software.

"Until then, workers had to punch in at a time clock. Every worker had a card that he inserted into the clock when he arrived at work and when he left for the day. At the end of the month, the information stamped on the worker's card was manually added up to see how many hours he had worked and how much he should be paid. Now they wouldn't have to do that anymore.

"I became a very wealthy man. And then, you'll be surprised to hear, I suddenly did have friends. But I was smart enough to realize that they weren't my friends because of who I was but because of the money I had. Still, it didn't matter to me. The main thing was that I had friends.

"One day, two of my friends asked me to become their partner in a business venture, and I was persuaded to do so. I soon found out that their only 'business' was to get as much money out of me as possible, which they managed to do to the point where my real business collapsed.

"I closed my company and had no success starting it up again because the field of computerized tracking had taken off and there was already competition. Though I knew what to do and how to do it, I no longer had the investment capital it would take to start again. I got a job with a company in the same field. The salary was very good, but not enough to make a person rich. About six months ago I retired, and since then I've been alone.

"I keep busy by volunteering in hospitals, but aside from that, I don't have anything going on in my life.

"I do have a few friends, but as you can see, they're not good enough friends to come to my seventieth birthday party.

"So there you have it. Please tell me, what good things can be said about me?"

* * *

"You're a very honest man," my father said, "and your story is touching. I think that it's very nice for a man like you, despite what he's been through, to volunteer at hospitals and care for others."

The father of the family that had joined us also said a few words of praise, and then we all joined in, each one of us saying something nice about him: some about him inviting us to join his birthday celebration, and some about him being a nice man who smiled, and some about the fact that he volunteered in hospitals (which was the best thing we learned about him).

Then my father said to me, "Now it's your turn, Yigal."

I didn't know what to say, so I decided to say what I felt at that moment.

"I don't really know you," I said, "but I was touched by your story. I'm in school, and when you told your story, I suddenly thought of a few boys who fit your description exactly. They don't have any friends, no one pays any attention to them, and sometimes they even get laughed at.

"I'm thinking right now of one boy in my class. Your story really reminds me of him. He doesn't have any brothers or sisters, and no one even knows where he lives. No one's ever gone to his house or invited him to theirs.

"I decided that from now on I'm going to do everything I can so that there won't be kids who grow up like that, where no one comes to their birthday party. I'm going to become friends with that boy and other boys who don't have friends."

People started clapping, but I stopped them.

"I think that it's not enough to make sure that that

boy in my class has friends. I feel sad about all the other children in the same situation. If you give me permission, I'll send your story to someone who publishes stories that reach hundreds of thousands of children. I think it will change the fate of hundreds of children, and it will all be thanks to you. The only thing left to ask is, do you agree?"

"Of course I agree!" the man said. "Not only don't I mind, but I'd be willing to talk to them myself and tell them about all I went through."

Then he asked me for the name of the place that publishes the stories.

"It's not a place," I told him. "It's a post office box, number 211. Children can send their stories there, and some of them are published in books called Kids Speak."

"Wonderful," the man said. "You can send in my story."

"But I'm not sure it will get published," I told him.

"Why not? Isn't it a good enough story?"

"I noticed that whoever publishes the stories likes a happy end, and..." I fell silent. What could I say to the man—that his story was so sad that it didn't even have a happy ending?

The man sat and covered his face with one hand. I think he was crying. I guess what I said brought him back to the terrible reality of his life. I felt bad that I had said it.

And then…we heard a noise at the entrance.

About a dozen elderly men came marching toward our table and cried out, "Mazel tov!"

The elderly man raised his head in shock, traces of tears still on his face.

"You thought we forgot, didn't you?" one said with a laugh. "Ha, ha, ha! Every year you invite us to your birthday party, but this time we decided to surprise you. We made up that all of us would arrive an hour later than the stipulated time, and asked the restaurant manager not to let you leave until we came.

"What do you think of the surprise?"

* * *

The elderly man gave a sad smile and told them, "I would tell you that this surprise is a very bad idea because it brought me very bad thoughts, but luckily I discovered some wonderful people who took pity on me and joined me for my birthday and brought me a lot of joy. Therefore, your unsuccessful surprise turned into a double surprise. I discovered the kindness in people, and I'm also going to be celebrating my birthday twice. One celebration ended right now, and as for the second, I'll tell the maître d' to set the table again, and we'll start the second birthday party celebration."

We wished him a happy birthday, said a warm goodbye to him as we each shook his hand, and began to move toward the exit.

Then I heard the old man call out, "Wait a minute! Yigal? That's your name, isn't it?"

Everyone in the restaurant fell silent.

"Now you have a good ending to the story, don't you?"

I nodded.

"So submit the story. You can title it, 'Seventy-Year-Old Kids Celebrate a Birthday.'"

We all laughed and then left the restaurant.

So now I'm sending the story to Kids Speak. I think that despite the happy ending, it's still a sad story, but I hope you will accept it anyway because it can better the lives of hundreds and thousands of children. If the children around them realize they should accept the child and include him, it might change his whole life — for the better.

The Answers in the Coat Pocket

My name is Naomi.

I'm twelve, and I'm in sixth grade.

I'm a happy, popular girl, but I've never excelled at school work.

Actually, saying I never excelled is a little bit misleading. The truth is, I'm a very weak student.

My parents took me for all sorts of evaluations and were told that I have the ability to do well, but I don't try hard enough.

My parents told me that this was good news, but for some reason, this good news didn't change my grades at all.

I moved up from grade to grade, and I guess you could say that I got used to being one of the laziest girls in the class.

My best friend's name is Etty. She's always smiling, and she's been my friend ever since first grade. I don't know if this is connected or not, but Etty is just like me in one other way: she also doesn't "excel."

For her too, "doesn't excel" means someone who gets grades like mine or even lower.

We even had a sort of half-joking, half-sad competition between us to see who would get the lowest grade.

It's important for me to make sure you understand that this wasn't a real competition and that neither of us was happy with low marks. We didn't go that far. We were smart enough to know that it wasn't okay to get grades like ours, and we wanted to improve, but for some reason, neither of us wanted it enough.

*   *   *

At the beginning of this year, everything changed.

We got an amazing teacher who everyone loved right away. Even Etty and me.

With me, that was as far as it went. But for Etty, it expressed itself in a far more significant way: she started paying attention in class, participating, doing homework, and studying for tests.

The result? Her marks rose from 60 to 70 to 80 and then to 100 on every test.

I was happy for Etty, but I must admit that I also felt a pang of jealousy.

Though she's my best friend, and I was happy for her that she was becoming a good student, I suddenly felt alone at the bottom of the class. That's how I thought of it.

I knew I could also make the effort; I could also pay attention in class and participate, do homework, and study for tests. But guess what? I didn't.

Though I really, really wanted to, and though my best friend had become a good student and I saw how good she felt about it, and though I felt alone at the bottom of the class, I still couldn't find the energy to start working hard.

*　　*　　*

During one of my special times with Ima, when the two of us sat over a cup of hot chocolate and talked, she said to me, "These past few days you've been preoccupied with something. What's happening, Naomi?"

"Remember that I told you that Etty started paying attention in class and getting good grades?"

"I remember. She's not happy about it?"

"She's very happy about it," I said. "She gets top marks on tests, and if she keeps it up, she's going to be one of the best students in the class."

"What's sad about that?" my mother asked. "Did she stop being your friend?"

"Not at all!" I said. "Why would she do that?"

"Then what about this makes you feel sad? She's your best friend; you should be happy for her. Now your best friend is one of the best students in the class."

"I know," I said. "And I'm happy for her, but…"

My mother waited for me to continue. She seemed interested and not at all critical.

"But since this happened, I feel like I'm the laziest girl in the class and the most unsuccessful. I also feel lonely." And then I said the line I made up: "I'm alone at the bottom of the class."

My mother didn't try to answer me. She listened put her arm around me. Then she hugged me tightly and said that she wanted to think about it and that we'd talk tomorrow.

The next day, we sat together again. My mother asked me if I had become lazier than before.

"Absolutely not," I said. "I even improved a bit, but I'm still lazy."

"So why do you feel sad?" my mother asked.

I didn't answer though the answer was on the tip of my tongue.

"You're sad because your friend became a good

student. There's no other explanation for your sad-
ness, and I'm not criticizing. It's human nature to feel
that way. It's not because you don't want to see her
succeed but because you now feel more keenly how
horrible it is not to succeed."

"Something like that," I said.

"Everything Hashem does is for the best," my
mother said. "Maybe this feeling will pave the way for
you to improve. Now you know that a girl who was
considered a lazy student can become a good one. Now
you believe that it's possible. The minute you decide to
march forward, you'll be following a paved path, and
it will be easier to reach your goal."

I felt encouraged by what my mother said, but it
still didn't prompt me to begin striding forward.

Then I got the first report card of the year.

*   *   *

Usually, Etty and I would hide our report cards
from the other girls in class and only show them to
each other with a bitter laugh.

This time Etty did not show me her report card.

And I knew why.

Not because she was ashamed. But because she did
not want me to be ashamed.

I appreciated her sensitivity. Still…

I felt a crack in our friendship. We, who had been so close that we weren't ashamed to show each other our bad grades, suddenly could not share with each other anymore. She, because she didn't want to hurt me, and I...because suddenly, I was ashamed.

We didn't say a thing about it, and it became a kind of barrier between us. Was it the beginning of the end of our friendship?

But a week later, something happened that changed everything.

*   *   *

It was a test in Yahadus—a particularly difficult test.

Etty tried, as usual, to interest me in studying with her, and I, as usual, wriggled out of it.

She complained that the test was hard and that she felt she knew nothing. I can't explain it, but deep in my heart, I felt a sense of relief that I was ashamed to admit existed.

Then we took the test.

The classroom was quiet. We began to look at the questions.

I didn't know anything, but I felt that Etty, who

was sitting next to me, was also feeling tense.

Five minutes passed. I glanced at her exam and saw that she was not writing anything.

Suddenly she got up from her seat and went over to her coat, which was hanging together with the other coats on a rack behind the teacher at the front of the classroom.

It was obvious that she was taking out a page and looking at it. How was it obvious? She hid the page with the coat, and her eyes darted to see if the teacher saw.

She didn't see me, but I and some of our classmates saw the whole thing.

Then she took a tissue from the coat (the tissue was in another pocket, an outside one), and went back to her seat.

Then I saw her start to write energetically.

I was certain of it: Etty had all the review questions and answers in her coat pocket.

It all added up. She had complained that she didn't remember the material and was positive she'd fail the test, so she decided to cheat.

I'm not such a *tzadekes* that I was so horrified by that, but I felt something awful toward her. But I didn't know what.

A few minutes later she got up again and went to

her coat to look at the secret note. This time most of the class noticed, but naturally, no one said anything to the teacher.

The third time, the teacher noticed and asked, "Is there a problem, Etty?"

"No, everything's fine," Etty said, pulling out the entire pack of tissues and waving it so the teacher could see.

She wasn't lying, but it was a kind of deception. She led the teacher to believe that she had gone to the coat for the tissue when everyone could see that that wasn't what she was interested in.

I felt something I couldn't name. Was it anger? Hatred?

The fourth time she got up, the teacher said to her, "You don't have to go to your coat all the time. Just take the package of tissues and put it on your desk."

Etty had no choice. Her excuse was ruined, but she was already at the end of the test. Within three minutes she finished the test and handed it in, then left the classroom for the schoolyard like the other girls.

I got through the test somehow. For some questions, I wrote answers that made sense to me, and some I just didn't answer at all.

I finished at the bell and left the classroom with

a heavy heart. I saw Etty, but something stopped me from going over to her.

For the first time in my life, I felt very distant from her.

* * *

The next day the teacher returned our marked tests, and, as always, she praised the girls who did well on it, especially Etty.

It ate me up. I don't know why. If you work hard, you deserve the praise—though even that was hard for me to take. But now they were praising someone who'd cheated, and that I couldn't stand.

The bell rang for recess, and all the girls left the classroom. I was on my way out when the teacher stopped me.

"Please remain in the classroom," she said.

I sat down in front of her desk.

"I see that you're very upset, even angry," she said.

I didn't answer.

"I've noticed this for quite some time, but yesterday it became more obvious. Anyone can see on your face that you're tense and angry. Am I wrong?"

I didn't utter a word.

"Can I assume that this has to do with your best friend, Etty?"

I remained silent.

"Tell me, Naomi—does it bother you that she has become serious about her school work?"

"No!" I cried out. "I'm happy for her. It's not that."

Without meaning to, I revealed that it wasn't "that"—which meant it was something else.

The teacher noticed. "So, what *is* it if not that?"

I was silent.

She looked at me and said, "I know what it is, even if you don't."

I said nothing.

"It's because Etty cheated on the test yesterday, isn't it?"

I was shocked. How did she know? But I didn't even blink. I'm not a tattletale.

"You don't have to answer me. It's fine. You don't have to tattle on your friend. I just know."

I was confused. How did she know what was going on inside me? I was even more surprised that if she knew Etty had cheated, why didn't she disqualify her test? Not only that, but she even praised her in front of the entire class!

* * *

"Let me explain something to you," the teacher

said. "Etty made a very positive change, one that was not easy at all, as you know. But the test in Yahadus was hard for her. She asked me to excuse her from taking it, but I absolutely refused. I told her that she had listened in class and knew the material and that what she was just lacking self-confidence.

"During the test, I, like you and all the other girls in the class, saw that she was running to her coat all the time. And, like the rest of the class, I realized that she was copying. I thought of disqualifying her from the test, but I decided not to. I did not want to hurt her and jeopardize all she had achieved with such hard work, so I decided to hold back.

"But immediately after the test, I quietly called Etty over and asked her to show me the paper she had copied from. She did, and the secret was revealed.

"I want to show it to you."

The teacher stood up, went to the coat rack, and took Etty's coat. She reached into a pocket and pulled out the folded paper.

It was Etty's report card.

She opened the report card and showed it to me.

For the first time, I saw the report card that Etty hadn't wanted me to see.

It was what we call a "boring" report card, if you

know what I mean. In my wildest dreams, I'd never thought Etty would get straight As.

"Now do you understand?" the teacher asked me. "Etty didn't cheat. She just wanted to strengthen her belief in herself, so she went over to see the beautiful report card she had worked so hard to attain. Seeing it banished her fears and allowed her to concentrate and just write down the answers she knew and had forgotten due to her insecurity."

* * *

I felt a cold chill sweep over me.

Naturally, I apologized to Etty for wrongly suspecting her.

"After I told the teacher," Etty said, "I asked her for one thing: to tell you the whole story and to show you the report card. I think you'll understand. I think that report card can encourage you to follow in my footsteps.

I felt tears fill my eyes. What a special, wise friend I have! Suddenly, I wanted to be like her and felt confident that I could do it, too. But the weakness she revealed in this story gave me the strength to believe that my weakness could also disappear somehow if only I'd believe in myself and try.

I won't bore you with the details. I followed the

path Etty had paved, just like my mother had predicted. Etty helped me pull myself up, and my mother and the teacher pushed me from below, but the path forward I did myself.

Without realizing it, Etty and I became even better friends than before.

And a month ago, we showed each other our final report cards.

This time, for the opposite reason.

Being the Real Me

My name is Yehudah.

I'm ten, and I live in Elad.

It's not easy for me to tell this story. But because I think it will help other kids, I decided to tell it anyway.

The story began about half a year ago. I went with three friends to a deserted area near our neighborhood. It's a large, empty tract of land almost half the size of our city. We usually stay away from it, but this time we let ourselves walk a little bit farther than we usually did. After about twenty minutes of walking, we saw a small concrete building. It looked strange to us. What was it doing in the middle of all this empty land?

We walked closer to the building. When we got to the entrance, we didn't know whether to go inside. The building was obviously abandoned because it didn't even have a door. On the other hand, an abandoned, neglected building—it's scary!

Then my friend Daniel suggested that we turn the building into a clubhouse just like the one Team Taryag made.

Like thousands of children, we too had dreams of making our own group. The problem was that we didn't find any exciting adventure to justify it. Now Daniel gave us the first challenge.

We went inside. It was a small, dark room without even a window. Really strange. Some light shone in through the entrance, but not much. It was dark. And the farther in we went, the darker it got.

We stood in silence, scared, and I couldn't see a single one of my friends.

"Daniel?" I called.

"Yes."

"Shalom?"

"Yes."

"Efraim?"

No answer.

"Efraim?" I called again, this time louder.

No answer.

It started to scare me, and I guess my friends too. Efraim was the first one in. He was always the bravest, but now he wasn't answering. Maybe someone else was in the clubhouse!

"Efraim!" the three of us called.

No answer.

And then...

We heard a frightening roar. We ran out, panic-stricken, screaming in fear. We ran a little and then stopped and turned to look back in shock at the clubhouse. We were three instead of four. Where was Efraim?

Suddenly he came out of the entrance, all smiles. "I pulled a good one on you!"

He'd hidden in a corner and hadn't answered when we'd called. Then he'd let out a terrifying roar that frightened us.

It took us time to calm down and get back to normal. He'd really scared us.

"It wasn't right to do that," I told him. "You scared us to death. We were sure that something had happened to you and that someone was hiding in there."

"You wanted Team Taryag, you got Team Taryag," he said. "Admit that it was an adventure!"

It was hard for us to admit that. We were really mad at him. But as time went by, we calmed down and even started to laugh at what had happened.

We decided to go there the following day as well.

"But what will we do there in the dark?" Efraim asked.

"I'll bring a big flashlight so we can see the inside of the clubhouse."

"That's a great idea," Daniel and Shalom said. "But we don't have any flashlights."

"Then let's bring candles," I said.

"Not a bad idea," they agreed. "We'll bring candles."

"Tomorrow at five o'clock."

We went our separate ways, looking forward to tomorrow.

* * *

The next day at five we were all there. We turned on the flashlight, lit the candles, and went inside.

It looked a lot less scary, though the place was still abandoned and neglected.

"We'll have to clean up the clubhouse before we can use it."

"Right," we all said. "Tomorrow we'll bring a broom and do some cleaning."

The next day we were in for a surprise. The place was clean.

"I know who must have cleaned it," Daniel said. "It was Yehuda." He pointed to me.

"Who said it was me?" I said. After all, I hadn't cleaned the clubhouse.

They understood from what I said that it was me but that I just didn't want to admit it.

"Great job!" Shalom said. "You made us a surprise. I stand in awe. I wouldn't dare come here alone. I'd be too scared."

I could have said, "What do you mean? It wasn't me!" I don't know why, but I didn't say anything. I think I was enjoying the compliments too much to give them up.

As if to second my thoughts, Efraim said, "Yehuda's been the leader from the beginning. The idea to bring a flashlight and candles was his, too."

You can imagine how good I felt. Why ruin it?

The next day we got there full of enthusiasm, excited about planning an adventure. We had a surprise waiting for us inside. Actually, three surprises: a table and two chairs.

"Listen, Yehuda, you're great!" the boys said one after the other. "How did you carry everything here? I'm in shock!" Shalom said.

You realize even without me saying it that I didn't bring a single thing there and that I had no idea how the table and chairs had gotten there. But I was used to not rejecting a free compliment when it came my way, so I humbly remained silent.

We sat there, two of us on the chairs and two on the table, and made plans.

The next day there was a chess set on the table. Naturally, I got compliments. The boys asked me, "What's going to await us here tomorrow?"

But my lips were sealed. They took that to mean that I wanted to surprise them, but you know the truth. I had no idea what was going to happen tomorrow, so I chose to keep quiet.

The day after that there was a lamp with rechargeable batteries. That was huge. We no longer needed a flashlight: just push the button, and the clubhouse lit up.

Over the next few days, two chairs and a small cabinet were added. Now the place was ready to be used as a real clubhouse.

Of course, my standing was sky high. My friends saw me as a guy with unlimited abilities. Only I knew that I hadn't brought a single one of those things.

I had a sinking feeling in the pit of my stomach.

I'm not stupid. I knew that if I hadn't brought those things, then someone else had. I knew all too well that the day would come when the other kids would know the truth. And when they found out, all their compliments would disappear in a flash, just like turning on the lamp (that I didn't bring) had made all the darkness in the clubhouse disappear.

I knew the day would come, and I dreaded it.

The fear was there not only when I was in the clubhouse where there were a lot of happy moments because I felt as strong as could be, but also at different moments. I felt weak because I knew that my feelings of strength weren't real.

* * *

One day my fears were realized.

Like always, we went together to the clubhouse. My friends tried to guess what surprise I'd prepared for them (and I quietly tried to guess, too). We entered the clubhouse and met two bigger boys – eighth graders from our school.

One of them was a strong, tall boy named Avichai. And the other was…none other than my older brother, Shimon.

* * *

"What are you doing here?" Avichai asked.

I didn't say anything, but Daniel spoke up.

"Excuse me? The question is, what are you doing in our clubhouse?"

"Your clubhouse, huh?" Avichai chuckled. "First of all, I'm happy to meet the new club, and I'm even happier to know that this place has turned into a clubhouse. And I'm happiest of all that you think this clubhouse belongs to you. But I've got one question, if you don't mind: What makes you think that this place is yours?"

"What do you mean?" Efraim asked. "We discovered it."

"As you can see, we're here too," my brother Shimon said. "What makes you think you were here first?"

Shalom said the words I'd been dreading. "Who do you think brought all the stuff you see here—the table and chairs, the lamp and everything?"

"Who brought it?" Shimon asked.

"We did!" Shalom declared triumphantly.

"You brought the table and chairs?" Shimon asked angrily.

I was the only one who knew how justified his anger was.

"Uh, it wasn't me exactly," Shalom said.

"Was it you?" Shimon asked Efraim and Daniel.

"No, it wasn't us. Yehuda brought it."

The moment I'd dreaded had arrived.

I knew just what was going to happen. How? Because I'd been dreading this moment every hour of every single day since the first lie. I knew that this moment would arrive, but I never dreamed that my downfall would come through my brother Shimon, of all people.

Shimon looked at me, and I looked at him. We were close enough brothers for Shimon to grasp in a flash everything that had happened there recently. He realized that I… had lied to my friends. That I'd pretended to be the one who brought everything there.

All the boys looked at Shimon, and I shook inside in fear of the truth that would destroy my image in my friends' eyes and turn me into a laughingstock.

But Shimon said, "Even if Yehuda brought all these things, it still doesn't make this clubhouse yours. But you know what? Enjoy it, and we'll think about what to do.

"Let's go, Avichai," he said to his friend. "We'll go home. We're in a rush anyway."

A wave of relief washed over me. My brother had saved my life. I knew that he and Avichai knew the truth all too well. But they'd chosen not to humiliate me in front of my friends.

We were left there by ourselves. My friends were drunk with victory.

"Good thing we proved to them that we were here first," Daniel said. Everyone said he was right. Everyone except me, who didn't agree with him.

* * *

Somehow, I got through the next half hour or so, and then I said, "I've got to get home now. Let's go."

We left the clubhouse and headed back. When we got to our neighborhood, we split up, and I went home. Shimon was waiting for me. Of course he would be waiting for me.

"So, Yehuda," he said, "was it hard to carry the table by yourself?"

I couldn't look him in the face. I felt so ashamed.

But he started to laugh. He stood up, gave me a hug, and said, "Yehuda, Yehuda, my sweet brother. You're such a big liar, but at least you're a lucky liar. Next time you won't have such good fortune because you won't be facing your brother but someone else who will use the opportunity to grind you to dust."

Despite the hurtful words, I felt the love behind them. I knew that Shimon would rescue me even if it meant a sacrifice on his part. I knew that those words he'd said were for my benefit even though they stung.

"Listen to me, Yehuda. You're still a kid, but you

have to understand that to be big and important and strong is only possible with the truth. Never with lies. This kind of self-confidence is something that can only be achieved with real efforts and not by pretending."

"You're right, Shimon, but...I don't know...I got messed up there."

I told him what had happened, and Shimon understood me perfectly.

"It was a test," he said. "If you had corrected this mistake at first, you would have gotten out of it. But because of one minute's confusion, you sunk deeper and deeper into your lie. And with less mazel, the lie would have been discovered in a different way, and the boys would have lost their trust in you.

"You know, Yehuda, there are a lot of kids who rule over their classmates forcefully, and the other kids think these bosses are the strongest and that they're the weakest. But it's enough for one boy or a few boys to decide to upset the apple cart, and then everyone sees that their power wasn't real. They were only acting as if they were strong when they were really the weakest kids in the world. How do I know? Because strong kids never hurt other people. The minute someone hurts someone else, it shows that he's weak. That's something every kid who feels he's weak should know. All they need to do is wait for the day it will all come to light.

"I hope, Yehuda, that you learned your lesson. You can be stand out and be impressive, but only with the truth. Never with lies.

"I'll work things out with Avichai, and you'll have to work things out somehow with your friends so that we can use the place too. Deal?"

"Deal," I said.

Shimon turned to leave and then I called him. "Shimon!"

He turned around.

"Uh, I really…uh…I really want to thank you. You…you saved me."

Shimon smiled. "It's okay," he said. "First and foremost, I am your brother. If you had been humiliated, it would have embarrassed me too. What's important is that you learned your lesson. I'm happy you didn't have to pay a heavy price for it."

That's the story. I learned a lot from it. Only if you stick to the truth can you be at peace with yourself, and only then can you be truly strong.

Glossary

The following glossary provides a partial explanation of some of the Hebrew, Yiddish, and Aramaic words and phrases used in this book. The spellings and definitions reflect the way the specific word is used in this book. There may be alternate spellings and meanings for the words.

baruch Hashem: thank G-d.

bas mitzvah: the celebration at age twelve when a Jewish girl is obligated to observe mitzvos.

b'ezras Hashem: G-d willing.

chas v'shalom: G-d forbid.

cherem: excommunication.

chinuch: education.

chutzpahdik: insolent.

Ima: mother.

kever: grave.

kibbud av va'eim: the mitzvah to honor and respect one's father and mother.

kiddush Hashem: sanctifying G-d's Name publically.

kivrei tzaddikim: burial sites of the righteous.

lashon hara: a remark that belittles or harms another person; gossip.

lishmah: for its own sake, without thought of reward.

mashal: parable.

mazel: blessing from Above.

middos: character traits.

mitzvah/mitzvos: commandment(s).

neshamah: soul.

oneg Shabbos: a gathering on Shabbos that includes inspiriation, singing, and refreshments.

oy larasha, v'oy lischeno: woe to the evildoer and woe to his neighbor.

rav: Rabbi.

rebbi: teacher.

rechilus: gossip.

Sefer Tehillim: Book of Psalms.

shelo lishmah: not for its own sake but with thought of reward.

simchah / simchos: joyous occasion

sinas chinam: hatred of another without cause.

siyata d'Shmaya: Divine assistance.

tehillim: psalms.

tzaddik: pious man or boy.

tzadekes: pious woman or girl.